All-Color

Mammals
of the World
Mary Parker Buckles

A Ridge Press Book

Bantam Books
Toronto·New York·London

Photo Credits

A = Ardea
BC = Bruce Coleman
MS = Miami Seaquarium

O = Tierbilder Okapia, Frankfurt
PR = Photo Researchers

Des Bartlett (BC): 79; Jen & Des Bartlett (BC): 116, 133; I. & L. Beames (A): 48; Bubenik (O): 51; Mary Parker Buckles: 8, 56, 141; Chambers (O): 49; Bruce Coleman: 30; Bruce Coleman, Inc.: 4–5, 53, 55; Werner Curth (A): 69; E. R. Degginger: 86, 91; Deschryver (O): 58; K. W. Fink (A): 23, (BC): 21, (National Audubon Society/PR): 89; Jeff Foott (BC): 119; Paul Germain (A): 31; S. V. Gooders (A): 150; P. W. Grace (PR): 27; Clem Haegner (A): 10, 85; J. A. Hancock (PR): 26; Hoffer (O): 109; Bill Hunter (MS): 128; Karl Kenyon: 121; Kirtley-Perkins: 82; G. L. Kooyman: 97, 99; J. W. La Tourrette (MS): 94; Richard J. Manly: 145, 146; J. Markham (BC): 29; Charles E. Mohr (National Audubon Society/PR): 88; Willard S. Moore: 20 (lt), 63, 98; Norman Myers (BC): 140, (O): 28, 59; National Parks Board of South Africa: 52 (rt); Ontario Ministry of Natural Resources: 22, 87; John Parkison: 110, 156; Mack Prichard: 73 (top); E. Hanumantha Rao: 78, 103; Hans Reinhard (BC): 114, 148, 155, (O): 24, 74, 90; Douglas Rod: 77; Jim Rod: 73 (btm); Root (O): 12, 19, 34, 39, 44, 54 (lt), 60, 64, 76, 108, 122; Leonard Lee Rue, Jr. (BC): 147; Leonard Lee Rue III: 62, 68, 75, 111, 115, 149, (BC): 70; Leonard Lee Rue IV: 66, 81, 138; W. Ruth (BC): 120; San Diego Zoo: 15, 50, 84; Schmidecker (O): 38; Dr. U. Schmidt (O): 40 (lt & rt), 41; Smithsonian Institution Photographic Service: 20 (rt), 37 (lt), 47, 92, 113; M. F. Soper (BC): 139; Spangle (National Park Service): 42; Kojo Tanaka: 16, 54 (rt), 57, 93, 105, 107, 118, 142, 152; Tennessee Wildlife Resources Agency: 80, 100, 112; Nancy Turel: 52 (lt), 104, 124, 130, 132, 137, 143, 153; Richard Waller (A): 126; J. Wallis (BC): 18; Peter Ward (BC): 32; Caroline Weaver (A): 151; John Wightman (A): 144; T. A. Willock (A): 134; Wisconsin Dept. of Natural Resources: 83; Wissenbach (O): 43; Jim Yoakum: 154; Robert Zappalorti: 37 (rt), 106.

Front Cover: Gorilla, Keystone Press Agency Ltd.
Back Cover: Giraffe, R. Austing (BC)
Title Page: Tasmanian Devil, K. W. Fink (A)
Facing Page: American Black Bear, Bill Browning

MAMMALS OF THE WORLD
A Bantam Book published by arrangement with The Ridge Press, Inc.
Designed and produced by The Ridge Press, Inc. All rights reserved.
Copyright 1976 in all countries of the International Copyright Union
by The Ridge Press, Inc. This book may not be reproduced
in whole or in part by mimeograph or any other means, without permission.
For information address: The Ridge Press, Inc.
25 West 43rd Street, New York, N.Y. 10036
Library of Congress Catalog Card Number: 76-9397
Published simultaneously in the United States and Canada.

Bantam Books are published by Bantam Books, Inc.
Its trademark, consisting of the words "Bantam Books" and the
portrayal of a bantam, is registered in the United States Patent Office
and in other countries. Marca Registrada.
Bantam Books, Inc., 666 Fifth Avenue, New York, N.Y. 10019.

Printed in Italy by Mondadori Editore, Verona.

Contents

Introduction

Mammals are important to human beings. Domestic species provide companionship, labor, and food. Wild species provide numerous products, including oil and leather. Yet we continue to exploit these close relatives of ours. Ironically, though, as more and more species disappear from the earth as a result of that exploitation, more and more human beings are coming to appreciate mammals on their own terms, apart from their contribution to our welfare.

Reactions to the findings of ongoing research in marine biology provide a prime example of the new attitude toward mam-

mals. This research has suggested that the communication systems and emotions of some cetaceans, dolphins in particular, may be much more complex than those of human beings, and that their highly developed sense of play indicates a comparably high level of intelligence. While such findings may threaten our sense of superiority among mammals, we are nevertheless becoming more and more intrigued with nonhuman species, and continue to grow in our appreciation of them for their own sake. This is the real frontier in the study of mammals, and the reason that mammals excite and challenge us as no other class of animals can.

5

California sea lions

Characteristics

Like the reptiles, fishes, amphibians, and birds, mammals are vertebrates—that is, they have backbones. But they also have several other characteristics that set them apart from, and in a sense above, all other animals.

Almost without exception, mammal offspring are born without the protection of an eggshell or other hard covering. Soon thereafter they begin to ingest milk, their sole food for some time. The production of milk for the young is a uniquely mammalian characteristic, and the one that gives mammals their name: *mamma* is the Latin word for "breast."

The nourishment an offspring receives during the suckling period extends far beyond nutritional values. The parental care that often accompanies suckling (and, in some species, continues well past weaning) is a vital nurturing experience important to the total well-being of newborn mammals.

Mammals are the only animals that have bodies covered with hair or fur. For the most part, these "coats" act as insulators, which help to maintain a constant body temperature, usually no lower than 35° and no higher than 38° C. (Internal insulation in the form of blubber takes the place of hair or fur in most marine mammals.) This maintenance of a relatively constant body temperature is known as warm-bloodedness. Shared by birds and mammals, it is significant because it enables those animals to be relatively independent of external temperatures, and therefore to live in almost all parts of the earth.

Other mammal characteristics include a four-chambered heart, a diaphragm, and specialized bones in the middle ear and lower mandible. Mammals also have specialized red blood cells which permit oxygen to be readily absorbed.

Classification

Altogether there are about twelve thousand living mammal species. Such a large number would be difficult to discuss and examine had scientists not come up with some system of classification, or a way of looking at mammals in smaller, more manageable groups. These groups are determined on the basis of the internal and external characteristics that particular mammals share. It is important to realize that mammals do not *belong* in certain groups, but have simply been described that way for the sake of convenience. The study of classification makes up an entire branch of biology known as taxonomy.

This method of classifying mammals, based on subdivision according to similarities, works as illustrated in the following example. All mammals are part of a large group of animals known as a class, the class Mammalia. Marsupialia, which includes the pouched mammals, is one of the nineteen orders of mammals within that class. Within the order are several families, one of which is Macropodidae, meaning ''big-footed'' in Latin. And within this family is a genus known as *Macropus*, from the same Latin root as the family name. Finally, within the genus *Macropus* is the species *rufus*, which means ''red'' in Latin. An animal's scientific name, or binomial, consists of the genus and the species: for the red kangaroo the binomial is *Macropus rufus*. (Both words are usually italicized.) Except in a few cases where further refinement is needed, the species is the basic unit of classification, and includes only those animals that interbreed regularly.

This type of classification serves at least two very sound purposes. First, the use of Latin affords a common terminology for scientists in all parts of the world, as it eliminates the various regional (and therefore confusing) names for a given animal. Second, familiarity with at least the general characteristics of the nineteen mammal orders is the first step toward reliable field identification.

The Latin nomenclature in this book is taken from Ernest P. Walker *et al., Mammals of the World*, 3rd edition (1975).

Adaptations

Ever since mammals began to develop along different lines from their reptilelike ancestors, some 200 million years ago, they have faced diverse habitats, enemies, climatic conditions, and a host of other environmental factors. Their various means of coping with these factors are the most vital, immediate aspect of mammal personalities. They are known as adaptations.

Closely related species that came to inhabit very different environments became adapted in quite different ways. For example, the marsupials of Australia have no doubt arisen from **7**

a common ancestor. Yet the different marsupial species are adapted differently, some to a rodentlike life style, others to a carnivorous one. Conversely, unrelated species that have come to inhabit similar environments have evolved similar adaptations. For instance, New World kangaroo mice and the springhare of Africa have developed in separate parts of the globe. Yet in response to similar habitats (sparsely vegetated desert), the two types of animals have evolved similar means of locomotion, a type of bipedal jumping that allows them to cover great distances quickly, in search of food.

Some mammals bear well-developed young, who can stand, walk, and run almost immediately after birth. These are usually species that live in the open, where parents are of no help if a quick escape is necessary. Other species, usually those that build nests or excavate dens for protection, bear blind, hairless offspring dependent on a parent for a relatively long period.

Adaptations used in self-defense include color and other types of camouflage, specialized body parts such as horns and quills, and behavior patterns ranging from threat displays to "playing 'possum." It is generally thought that a mammal is not born knowing how to react defensively to an enemy, but learns by mimicking its parents. Play sessions in which much defensive **8** and other learning occurs have evolved in the higher mammals.

Polar bear cub

Growth rate, normal life span, and body size of a given species are all determined by a combination of genetic and environmental factors. So is hibernation, the body state that evolved to accommodate certain nonmigratory mammals that live in very cold areas. While many mammals go into a deep winter sleep, few species actually hibernate. Those that do, experience dramatic physiological changes—body temperature and heartbeat drop severely, and breathing slows down and becomes irregular. Usually a hibernating mammal is in so deep a torpor that it is difficult if not all but impossible to arouse.

No adaptation is more important to a mammal's welfare than its means of locomotion. Most mammals are quadrupeds—that is, they move on all four feet. Some of the slower-moving quadrupeds place the entire foot firmly on the ground every time they take a step. This method of walking is called plantigrade, and it enables polar bears, for instance, to maintain a firm grip on ice. Faster-moving quadrupeds such as the big cats move digitigrade—on only the tip of the foot, or the digits. This allows them to take off quickly and to run at high speeds. Ungulates actually walk on their toenails, or hooves. In the case of mountain goats, climbing and gripping slick inclines would be impossible were it not for the specialized hooves.

Human beings are the only mammals that consistently walk bipedally. Some of the other primates can walk this way for short distances, at which times they may use their front feet in food-gathering or in other ways that resemble the uses of human hands. Most kangaroos walk on all fours, but jump bipedally and sit upright, using their tails like a third leg, for extra support.

Mammals that spend most of their time off the ground have their own types of adaptations for getting about. Some of the primates have very strong forearms, which they use in swinging from branch to branch. Bats, of course, fly, and several other mammals glide through the air. Marine mammals are adapted to movement in the water not only by flippers and fins, but also by -their streamlined bodies, which minimize water resistance.

A mammal's diet is determined largely by its specialized teeth. Tooth specialization, by equipping different mammals for individualized diets, helps to reduce competition for food among species. Mammal teeth are of four basic types. The **9** incisors, in the center of the mouth, are highly developed in gnawing mammals such as beavers. The canines, or eyeteeth, are well developed in mammals such as carnivores, who use them to pierce and tear their prey. The premolars and molars, together referred to as the cheek teeth, are highly developed in the grazers (mammals that eat grass and other ground-level vegetation) and the browsers (mammals that eat vegetation growing above ground level). Some grazers have numerous molars, each with several subdivisions called cusps, which grind nonwoody vegetation. The labels carnivore (meat-eater), herbivore (plant-eater), and omnivore (meat- and plant-eater), while handy and certainly accurate to some extent, do not allow for the many local, seasonal, and other variations in a mammal's diet and therefore should not be applied too rigidly.

Adaptations that help mammals communicate are often multipurpose. For example, territorial markings may serve to attract mates as well as to keep enemies away. Vocalizations such as roaring notify individuals of each other's presence and in some cases also strengthen social bonds. Signals that warn of danger can be visual or auditory. And there are doubtless communication networks still unraveled by the human imagination.

Springhare

Distribution and Environment

Mammals are not scattered randomly over the earth. Rather, each species appears in the habitat or habitats to which it is adapted. A habitat is a particular combination of available food and water, available shelter, and climatic factors that surround a community of living things. It is because of their dependence on habitat that mammal species are vulnerable to pressures from human beings. We continue to destroy habitats, as well as to interrupt predator-prey relationships through unregulated hunting and through such practices as poisoning, poaching, and trapping. In many cases the land's carrying capacity—the amount of life that the land can support—has been very heavily taxed through man's lack of foresight.

It is estimated that two-thirds of the mammal species that have ever lived on earth are now extinct, many as a result of human exploitation. Among those extant, many are seriously threatened. Once they are gone, these species cannot be re-created. Rather, because of the interdependence of all plant and animal life, their extinction will probably be followed by the extinction of others, possibly even *Homo sapiens*, and the richness and variety of the planet will be forever diminished.

* * * *

This book is not a field guide; rather, it is an introductory sampling of the types and habits of the many mammal species. Its geographic scope is worldwide, and only wild (that is, un-domesticated) species are included. The book is organized by orders, beginning with the most primitive, or those that evolved the earliest. The species pictured include representatives of all nineteen mammal orders, and representatives of each family within the smaller orders. Some of the orders that contain a great many families are divided into suborders and, where possible, a representative of each suborder is included. Average adult sizes of the species pictured are given in the captions.

Most of the scientific terms used in the text are defined in the Introduction. The definitions of a few others, incorporated into the text itself, may be found through the Index. Family names (which end in "ae") are given in the text where they are of particular significance. Further information on families may be found in some of the books listed in the Bibliography. **11**

Monotremata

Monotremes are unique among mammals. Very early in the process of mammal evolution they somehow became isolated from the mainstream of development. Consequently, they retain more characteristics of their reptilian forebears than the other mammal species do, and are not themselves considered true ancestors of the marsupials and placentals. (The little that is known of monotreme ancestry has been deduced from extremely scanty fossil records.)

Of all mammals, the monotremes alone lay eggs instead of bearing live young. The eggs are fertilized within the female's body; then they are laid, incubated, and hatched. Their shells resemble reptile shells in that they are leathery and somewhat pliant, not hard like birds' eggshells. Like reptiles and birds, monotremes have a cloaca, a single chamber used in both elimination and reproduction. (The higher mammals have evolved more complex ways of carrying out these functions.) Certain skull and eye structures, the presence of a shoulder girdle, and some characteristics of the backbone and ribs are also rather reptilian, as are the overall posture and carriage of each of the species.

In contrast to their more reptilelike features, the monotremes do possess some typical mammal characteristics, including body hair, a four-chambered heart, and a high percentage of DNA in their cells. The spiny anteater has a relatively large brain, and its sperm resembles the sperm of higher mammals in several important respects. More interestingly, monotremes have two characteristics that fall somewhere between those of the true reptiles and those of the higher mammals. One is their imperfectly regulated warm-bloodedness, which is due to **13**

Duck-billed platypus, 500 grams–2 kg

an inconsistent body temperature that normally fluctuates between 22° and 35° C. In addition, the females have mammary glands but lack true mammary organs. Newborns get their nourishment not through sucking, but simply by lapping up the milk that oozes onto the mother's abdominal fur or into a pouch.

For the sake of convenience, mammals are sometimes grouped into subclasses. The subclass Prototheria includes all the living monotremes, the subclass Theria, all other mammals. (The Theria may be subdivided even further, to differentiate pouched mammals from placentals.)

The order Monotremata contains two families. The duck-billed platypus belongs to the family Ornithorhynchidae, members of the two genera of spiny anteaters to the family Tachyglossidae. All monotremes inhabit the Australian region.

Duck-billed Platypus

Ornithorhynchus anatinus

A moist, leathery bill endowed with an extraordinary sense of touch guides the platypus along fresh-water lake and stream bottoms, where it feeds on crustaceans, mollusks, and various insect larvae. (The eyes and ears close when the animal submerges.) Both the bill and the broadly webbed feet are used by the female as she excavates her nesting burrow, which may be up to 18 meters long, in a bank. Together the female and her mate create a second, less elaborate burrow, occupied by the male alone during the breeding season. As a precaution against flooding, platypuses put their chamber entrances well above water level.

After an early autumn courtship and mating, the female takes several bundles of wet leaves into her nesting burrow. These will provide moisture to keep her two soft-shelled eggs from drying out. Then she secludes herself inside the burrow by plugging the chamber entrance with mud. Two weeks after mating, the eggs are laid, and are incubated for approximately ten days before they hatch.

Platypuses have been avidly sought for their fur and were once in danger of extinction. Today, however, they are protected throughout their range in Tasmania and eastern Australia.

Spiny anteater, 5.5–6 kg

Spiny Anteater

Tachyglossus aculeatus

The spiny anteater, also called the echidna, is one of the few animals that can dig itself almost completely out of sight when threatened. If the soil is too hard or rocky for its broad feet to dig into, the echidna simply rolls itself into an impenetrable ball or takes shelter in a rock crevice.

During the breeding season the female echidna develops a special pouch on her underside. After she produces her single egg, she carries it in the pouch until it hatches. For six to eight weeks thereafter the offspring remains there, where it laps up the thick milk that oozes from specialized glands. Because the female echidna has no nipples, her offspring cannot actually be said to suckle.

Except for man, the echidna has no known enemies throughout its range (Australia and New Guinea). Nevertheless, the male echidna, like the male platypus, can defend itself with venom from a spur on its hind legs.

Marsupialia

Marsupial females have no placentas, but most have pouches into which their poorly developed newborns move just after birth. There they continue to develop. If no pouch is present, as with the numbat, the young cling to the hair on the mother's abdomen. In either case, each tiny newborn attaches itself to a nipple, which swells in its mouth and helps keep it in place as it suckles.

Most marsupials live in Australia, where about 120 species have been classified.

Koala

Phascolarctos cinereus

The appealing koala is a prime candidate for extinction—its soft fur was once avidly sought after; its specialized diet of eucalyptus leaves makes it a difficult species to take from its native habitat to zoos; and it has a low birth rate—it takes three or four years for an individual to reach sexual maturity, and it bears only one offspring per year. Yet, thanks to an active conservation program, koalas are on the increase in their native eastern Australia.

The koala has a complex digestive system, which uses soil and gravel to grind the bulky eucalyptus leaves and plays an important role in weaning: when her offspring is about six months old, the mother produces a predigested substance instead of milk. The young koala laps this from her anus and is weaned after about a year. Toward the end of this period it rides its mother piggyback.

Koalas' forelimbs are adapted for grasping, the first two digits being opposable to the other three. Koalas sleep in the forks of trees during the day and rarely descend to the ground. **17**

Koala, 4–15 kg

Thick-tailed Dormouse Possum

Cercartetus nanus

The dormouse possum is one of about six species of pigmy possums, all of which are no bigger than a mouse—10–30 grams. But they are easily distinguished from mice by their prehensile (grasping) tails, which are usually carried in a relaxed curled position. Dormouse possums are known to use their tails in climbing, and even to hang by them when necessary. One of the two *Cercartetus* species bears the common name thick-tailed dormouse possum because of its tail's capacity to store fat and thus become enlarged during the winter, when these marsupials go into a state similar to hibernation.

Like its namesake the dormouse, this pigmy possum is nocturnal. It feeds mainly on nectar and insects, and it shelters in the hollows of trees. Little is known of its reproductive patterns.

Dormouse possums inhabit Tasmania and the coastal areas of southwestern and southeastern Australia. They belong to the diverse family Phalangeridae, along with the pigmy possum *Burramys parvus*, which was ''discovered'' live in Victoria in 1966. Before that time, scientists had seen only fossils of this marsupial, and it was assumed that the species had been extinct for at least twenty thousand years.

▲ Thick-tailed dormouse possum, 15–25 grams
Coarse-haired wombat, 15–30 kg ▶

Coarse-haired Wombat

Vombatus ursinus

Wombats look like small bears, but have long rodentlike incisors. The two pairs of teeth grow continually and are kept worn down with use. Strict vegetarians, wombats prefer to eat fresh stems, which they uproot with their front feet.

These solitary animals dig elaborate burrows and defend them vigorously against predators. If hissing does not repel a would-be intruder, kicks with the powerful hind legs almost always will. Wombats bear their single offspring in a chamber of the burrow lined with bark and leaves. For several weeks the youngster stays in its mother's pouch, which, because it opens toward the rear of her body, stays clean of soil as the female digs.

Only two wombat species exist. The common, or coarse-haired, species differs from the soft-furred species in its hairless nose, rounded ears, and lack of underfur beneath the short, harsh coat. In both, coloration varies somewhat with locale.

Coarse-haired wombats live in southeastern Australia, Tasmania, and Flinders Island (in Bass Strait). They may live in or near towns, but because they are nocturnal, they are seldom seen in their natural habitat.

Kangaroos

Red Kangaroo, *Macropus rufus*
Great Gray Kangaroo, *Macropus giganteus*

Kangaroos are the largest living marsupials. With the wallabies they make up the family Macropodidae, which means "big-footed." Their large hind limbs are adapted for bipedal jumping, and along with the sturdy tail (a balancing aid), enable these marsupials to perform their characteristic leaps. They are also mighty weapons in spars between rival bucks, as are the clawed short front feet, which are used in normal walking.

The doe bears a single joey, which stays in its mother's pouch for about six months, then suckles from outside the pouch for a few more months. Shortly after one joey is born, another is conceived. The development of this second embryo is slowed while the pouch remains occupied. One day after the pouch is vacated, the second joey is born.

Red kangaroos actually vary in color from red to gray. They are distinguished from the great gray and other species by their black-and-white muzzle markings and the pale tip of the tail. Great grays are found in Australia's forests, red kangaroos in the grasslands, where the pet-food industry and sheep farmers, among others, continue to exploit them unmercifully.

▲ Great gray kangaroo, 25–65 kg
Red kangaroo, 25–65 kg ▶

Matschie's Tree Kangaroo

Dendrolagus matschiei

Tree kangaroos are well adapted to their niche. On the soles of their feet they have naked pads helpful in gripping branches, and their foreclaws are long and curved, perfect for digging into bark (tree kangaroos descend backward down the trunks of trees). The tail may act as a brace during climbs. On the ground, tree kangaroos hop much like the larger terrestrial species, with the body held forward to counterbalance the long, evenly furred tail. They leap huge distances, often 9 meters from one tree to a lower tree, and as much as 18 meters from tree to ground.

These marsupials feed on leaves and fruit, which they pluck directly from the trees. They sleep in small groups in the branches, where they are safe from most dangers. Tree kangaroos, in fact, have no predators capable of climbing trees. Thus, while they themselves do not climb particularly well, they are nonetheless agile enough to secure food, the only real survival pressure on them while they are off the ground.

Matschie's tree kangaroo is one of five species of tree kangaroos found in New Guinea. Two additional species inhabit northeastern Queensland, Australia. All seven are hunted for their meat by the aborigines, who flush them from the treetops and grab them by their tails.

Matschie's tree kangaroo, 6.5 – 7.5 kg

North American Opossum

Didelphis virginiana

The sole North American marsupial, the Virginia opossum, or North American opossum, has a prehensile tail. Along with the opposable toe on the hind foot, the tail helps in climbing, and is sometimes wrapped around leaves to transport them to a new nesting site. A young opossum may hang upside-down by its tail, but most adults do not.

Opossums do not seem to claim and defend territories in their woodland habitats, but bear their offspring in whatever tree trunk or other shelter is available. The young are born less than two weeks after conception, their bodies being less than half the size of a hummingbird. They pull themselves into the mother's warm abdominal pouch with their clawed front feet, where they attach themselves to her nipples. Their claws drop off shortly thereafter. They suckle from inside the pouch for about two and a half months, then move onto the mother's back, where they climb and ride for about thirty days. During this time they continue to nurse.

Opossums have fifty very sharp teeth, more than any other terrestrial American mammal, and they will accept nearly any type of food. This adaptation, along with the ability to ''play dead'' when threatened, probably accounts for the opossum's survival for some seventy million years.

These marsupials are found in North America from the southern part of Canada south into Central America.

Tasmanian Devil

Sarcophilus harrisii

"Devil," the name that white Tasmanian settlers gave this mammal, certainly seems to befit its personality. When disturbed, it reacts by snarling and coughing huskily, and its pale ears gradually turn to red. Though small (the larger males grow to only about 10 kilograms), it is equipped with teeth capable of crushing bone, and it will not hesitate to attack animals larger than itself and consume them, fur, feathers, bones, and all. It actually fills a carnivorous niche in its native Tasmania, and along with the native cats and several other species, is referred to as a "marsupial carnivore." Dingoes, bats, and seals, in fact, are the only native non-marsupial carnivores in the entire Australian area. This fact illustrates how the composition of the area's fauna is really a function of the continent's isolated position—carnivores and hoofed animals, plentiful in other parts of the world, simply never found their way across the oceans to Australia.

Tasmanian devils like the water, and seem to enjoy sunning, even though they are basically nocturnal. They move rather clumsily, with their tails elevated, among the dense underbrush of Tasmania, which is the entire extent of their range.

23

▲ Tasmanian devil, 4.5–5.5 kg (females), 6–10 kg (males)
◄ North American opossum, 2–5.5 kg

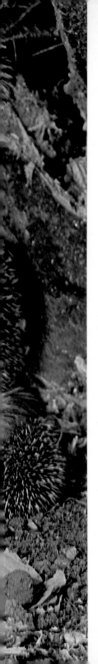

Insectivora

Moles, shrews, hedgehogs, and the bizarre-looking solenodons and tenrecs make up the order known as Insectivora, which means "insect-eater." All the members have long, thin snouts and clawed digits. They were the first animals to have placentas, which sets them apart from the monotremes and marsupials.

Insectivores occur in tremendous numbers throughout most of the world, yet because of their generally small size and nocturnal habits, they are seldom seen. The line between them and the early primates (tree shrews, for example) has never been clearly drawn.

Eurasian Hedgehog

Erinaceus europaeus

Gardeners and farmers throughout Europe value these mammals as a check on pests. When threatened, hedgehogs hiss and roll themselves into spiny balls. They are amazingly resistant to toxins, including those of the bees and wasps on which they feed. A hedgehog bitten by a viper usually dies, but a viper killed by a hedgehog can be eaten, venom glands and all, with no ill effects upon the hedgehog.

This mammal performs a curious "self-anointing" ritual, in which it spreads frothy saliva over its spines. The purpose of this is unknown, but the stimulus can be almost any strong-smelling substance, which the hedgehog licks until its saliva becomes foamy.

Eurasian hedgehogs hibernate restlessly from early fall to late spring in the colder parts of their large range. They breed at least twice a year, and, after a gestation period of about forty-two days, produce four or five offspring.

25

Eurasian hedgehog, 400 grams–1 kg

Cuban Solenodon

Solenodon cubanus

The zigzag path it takes through the forest, and its waddling walk, with much tripping over its own feet, are the trademarks of this peculiar little animal. Unfortunately, both solenodon species, Haitian and Cuban, are near extinction. This is due in part to their low reproductive rate—they usually bear no more than one or two young per annual (or sometimes semiannual) litter. They also face overwhelming predation by mongooses and by domestic species, mostly dogs and cats, that have been introduced onto their islands.

Although the tiny solenodon is hard-pressed for survival, it does have a defensive adaptation that is rare among mammals: it has poisonous saliva. A solenodon first bites its victim, then injects the wound with saliva, which flows from the large lower incisors. It is not known for certain whether a solenodon is immune to another solenodon's venom.

This nocturnal animal roots for food in the ground with its long snout, and in rotten logs with its foreclaws. Its diet consists of various small invertebrates and reptiles, along with some vegetable matter. A solenodon can rest on its haunches to feed if it props itself up with its long, very sparsely haired tail.

26

▲ Cuban solenodon, 300 mm long without tail (exact weight unknown)
Lesser American short-tailed shrew, 4–7 grams ▶

Lesser American Short-tailed Shrew

Cryptotis parva

Only about 80 millimeters long, shrews of the genus *Cryptotis* are the shortest American mammals. The adults weigh no more than 7 grams. By human standards this animal's rate of metabolism is extraordinary: every day it may eat more than its own weight in insects and other small animals, and along with members of the genus *Blarina* (the greater American short-tailed shrews) is considered a significant check on insects.

Cryptotis shrews are found throughout most of the eastern United States and as far south as northern South America. *C. parva* is the only one found north of Mexico. Unlike the more solitary *Blarina* species, it is gregarious—several adults will often share a nest of shredded vegetation. It stores some of its food in tunnels that have been excavated through communal effort, and it sometimes uses runways made by voles. The home range is much less than an acre.

Breeding begins when the female is only about three months old, and continues throughout the year in the more southern parts of the range. About two weeks after mating, a litter of three to six is born. The young are weaned in about twenty-one days.

Long-eared Elephant Shrew

Elephantulus sp.

Observers are tempted to think of elephant shrews as composite animals—legs like a kangaroo, a snout like an elephant, and the overall appearance of a jerboa. The eyes, very large for an insectivore, even give this mammal a mouselike appeal. But it has its own characteristics, and is well adapted to its various habitats throughout most of Africa.

Elephant shrews are so small (25–50 grams) that they shelter in cracks in the soil, especially those individuals that excavate no burrows. Those that do burrow may not always do the whole job themselves—some take over digging where a small rodent has left off. One or two relatively large young are born in the burrow, and may be carried about while still attached to their mother's nipples.

Members of the genus *Elephantulus* feed on insects and some plant material. They are somewhat gregarious, and use a common area for their excrement. Their movement is on all fours, even their agile leaps, which at one time were thought to be two-footed.

About eight species of *Elephantulus* exist. *E. rufescens* is a carrier of a type of malaria to which people seem immune. That **28** species and others have been used in malarial research.

Long-eared elephant shrew, 25–50 grams

Old World Water Shrew

Neomys fodiens

Water shrews, like the wholly terrestrial shrews, are amazingly active mammals. Found near lakes and streams throughout much of the USSR, Europe, and the Mediterranean countries, they dive repeatedly for food. They capture small amphibians, fishes, and some other aquatic animals; *Neomys fodiens* inactivates its prey with a poison it secretes. Although not equipped to live exclusively in the water, these insectivores can stay submerged for up to twenty seconds, and like the platypus, they rid their coats of excess water when they enter their burrows, the earth apparently acting like an absorbent sponge.

The two *Neomys* species are classified as members of the family Soricidae. The juveniles of other genera in this family have an unusual way of arranging themselves when they leave the nest. They line up behind their mother, and the offspring first in line grabs the mother's fur in its teeth. Each of the other siblings takes hold of the fur of the sibling in front of it in the same way. Their grip is so secure that people have been known to lift a mother into the air with all her offspring still attached.

Neomys shrew females bear between three and seven young at least twice a year. The life span of the species is not more than about a year and a half.

Old World water shrew, 12–18 grams

European Mole

Talpa europaea

The mole's stiffly clawed forefeet are much larger than its hind feet, and turn outward at all times. These provide the real burrowing power for this nearly blind mammal. Because its soft fur will lie in any direction, the mole can navigate both backward and forward in its tunnels. As it drills through the earth, it pushes aside loosened soil, which is prevented from entering its ears by specialized ear flaps.

Although the European mole will come aboveground, it usually forages in its network of subterranean chambers. It eats earthworms and insect larvae that it finds in the passageways. Those creatures it does not eat immediately it stores for winter food, first immobilizing them by snipping off body parts. (Moles have been known to hoard over a thousand live earthworms at a time, after having bitten them near the head to paralyze them partially.) A mole reputedly cannot go without eating for more than twelve hours.

It is interesting to note that the reproductive organs of both male and female moles (and some other mammals as well) are small and inactive for most of the year, and become enlarged only in early spring, just prior to the breeding season. The sexual passages of European mole females actually close after the breeding season, and stay sealed over with scar tissue until the next breeding time, when they reopen.

European moles inhabit Great Britain and most of Europe. They can be very quarrelsome animals, and the victor in a fight with another mole has been known to eat the loser.

Star-nosed Mole

Condylura cristata

The star-nosed mole is unique front and back. Twenty-two fleshy pink rays project from its nose and, except for two that are held rigid, are in constant motion as the mole searches for food. These rays, or tentacles, draw inward as the star-nose eats. The tail stores fat, which can be a lifesaver if fresh food becomes scarce in late winter or early spring. This adaptation (present in several mammals) is particularly important, since this mole does not hibernate but hunts for food year-round. It may even draw on its tail's reserve energy during the breeding season.

Paddlelike forefeet, strong hind legs, and waterproof fur equip this mole for the water, where it swims and dives with ease. It forages extensively underwater and eats earthworms, aquatic insects, crustaceans, and small fish. Not confined to its tunnels like many other moles, the star-nose moves aboveground, and may be seen on the snow in the colder parts of its range. Damp or muddy soil is its habitat throughout the eastern part of temperate North America.

▲ Star-nosed mole, 40–80 grams
◄ European mole, 60–110 grams

Dermoptera

The name "Dermoptera" is derived from the Greek words for "skin" *(derma)* and wing *(pteron)*. It is the only order made up entirely of gliding mammals. They are known as colugos or flying lemurs.

The single genus *Cynocephalus* has two species, which make up the whole order. *C. volans* is found in the forests of several Philippine islands, *C. variegatus* in southern Indochina and western Indonesia.

Colugo, or Flying Lemur

Cynocephalus variegatus

One hundred thirty-five meters is a long way for an animal to glide. Yet the flying lemur does it, and loses no more than 12–15 meters in elevation. What enables it to perform this feat is the furred membrane that extends from the neck to the webbed front and back feet, and on to the tip of the tail. Opened, it forms a parachute more well developed than that of the flying squirrels or phalangers.

Colugos often nest together during the day. They may hang from their sharp claws inside a hollow tree, or they may wrap their entire limbs around branches. In the evening they glide to their food trees, where they eat flowers, leaves, and fruits. *C. variegatus* has a penchant for coconut flowers, and some members of this species live in coconut groves in Malaya.

Zoologists have had difficulty classifying colugos, since they have features of both the insectivores and the lemurs. Their lower incisors, for example, resemble the lemurs' comb teeth, yet their skulls are very primitive. For reasons such as these they have been given their own order.

Flying lemur, 1–1.75 grams

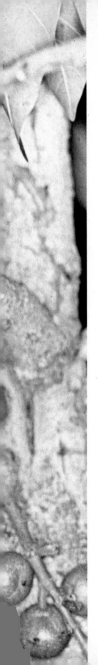

Chiroptera

Bats are the only mammals capable of true flight. Their "wing," called a patagium, is actually a membranous extension of the back and stomach skin, stretched over a skeleton of very long arms and fingers and relatively short legs. When a bat spreads its fingers, it becomes a sort of living kite, with the light, hollow finger bones serving as ribs.

When they are at rest during the day, or during hibernation, most bats hang head-down from hooked thumbs or from feet wrapped over branches. Takeoff is easy from this position. The bat simply releases its hold, drops a short distance, and spreads its wings to become airborne.

Echolocation is the process by which the majority of bats navigate and locate food. They send out high-frequency vocalizations that strike objects in their path and return to the sender as echoes. Bats probably communicate among themselves through body vibrations that produce sound.

Except for Rodentia, the order Chiroptera contains more species (some nine hundred in all) than any other order. These species are usually grouped into two main suborders. One of them, the Megachiroptera, is made up of members of the family Pteropodidae, which includes all the Old World fruit bats (about 130 species). The other suborder, the Microchiroptera, is made up of all remaining bats. Sometimes bats are further subdivided by diet—the insect-eaters, the fruit- and flower-eaters, the blood-suckers (vampires), and the meat- and fish-eating bats. The latter two groups contain the largest individuals, their maximum length being about 400 millimeters, excluding the tail. **35**

Flying fox, 600–900 grams

Flying Fox

Pteropus sp.

Flying foxes, with the exception of the rousette fruit bat and possibly the tube-nosed bats, do not echolocate. Nearly all the members of their family, the Pteropodidae (Old World fruit bats), have very large eyes with which they navigate; they locate food by smell. In the evening flying foxes may travel long distances to fruit trees, where they extract the juices from fruits, then spit out the pulp. (Their teeth are adapted to the soft diet.) Occasionally they swallow the fruit meat itself, and they sometimes feast on eucalyptus and other flowers. These bats can be serious pests to commercial fruit-growers.

After feeding for several hours, flying foxes return to the trees that they use as roosts year after year. Thousands of them may roost together there. They hang by the feet and the clawed second fingers of the arms, the characteristic posture of members of this family.

Flying foxes are so named because of their facial resemblance to foxes. They are among the larger bats, with a wingspan of up to 1.7 meters.

The genus *Pteropus* ranges from Madagascar to Southeast Asia, to the Philippines, eastern Australia, Fiji, and Samoa.

Hairy-tailed Bats

Hoary Bat, *Lasiurus cinereus*
Red Bat, *Lasiurus borealis*

Hairy-tailed bats often appear to be dead leaves, since they sway from side to side in the wind while hanging from branches. The hoary bat is a strong swift flier known to migrate in birdlike waves. It ranges over the mainland of the Americas, and is the only bat found in the Hawaiian Islands. Because it is somewhat rare, and because it avoids houses and other man-made structures, the hoary bat is seldom seen by people. But it can be heard "chattering" noisily during flight. This large member of the family Vespertilionidae is named for the frosty appearance of its dense coat. The fur is brownish with white or yellow tips, and presents quite an elegant appearance.

The handsome brick-colored red bat is found throughout most of the Americas and on several Atlantic and Caribbean islands. Because it frequently feeds on insects that gather around street lamps and other lights, it is seen fairly often. All dozen or so *Lasiurus* species breed during the summer and give birth in the spring. The actual gestation period, however, is thought to be only seventy-five to ninety days. After breeding, the female stores the sperm in her uterus over the fall and winter; fertilization and birth do not occur until the following spring. The red bat is the only bat thought to bear more than two young at a time—it has four mammae instead of the usual two. Blue jays prey heavily on red bat young where ranges coincide. It has been thought that before they are five or six weeks old, at which time they are ready to fly on their own, the offspring cling to their mother during her feeding flights. However, this seems unlikely, since the red bat often catches insects on the wing and would be hampered by the extra weight.

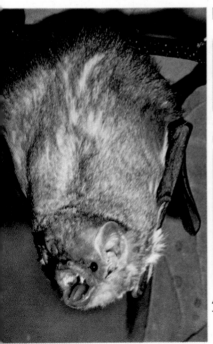
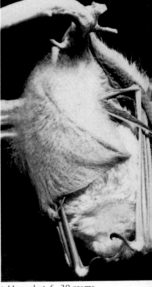

▲ Hoary bat, 6–30 grams
◀ Red bat, 6–30 grams

Dog-faced Fruit Bat

Cynopterus sp.

The three *Cynopterus* species are the only home-makers among Old World bats: they occasionally hollow out places to hang in the bunches of fruit that a certain type of palm produces. Groups of six or eight also roost in caves, as well as under the eaves of houses. Breeding usually occurs once a year in most of their range (from India to the Philippines), and a single young is born.

Cynopterus members often fly 100 kilometers or more for one night's feeding. They drain figs, guavas, palms, mangoes, and plantains of their juices. *C. sphinx* helps to disperse date-palm seeds through its droppings.

The ears of these fruit bats are typical of the Pteropodidae— simple, with no accessory lobes. They add to the bats' doglike appearance, whence the common name. In some areas dog-faced bats are eaten, or sold as medicine, since they are thought to impart strength to anyone who partakes of them. These and other superstitions have surrounded bats for as long as they have **38** been known.

Dog-faced fruit bat, 50–100 grams

Free-tailed Bat

Tadarida sp.

Long tails, free of membranous tissue, give these insectivorous bats their common name. Between forty and sixty *Tadarida* species inhabit most of the world's tropical and subtropical regions. Some free-tails share roosts with birds, others with scaly-tailed squirrels. Because of their musky odor, they can be a nuisance when they roost under the eaves of houses. The young of some *Tadarida* species are left in the roost during feeding flights. When the lactating females return, the offspring suckle indiscriminately, not necessarily from their own mothers.

One species of *Tadarida* roosts by the millions in the crevices of North America's Carlsbad Caverns. Their guano was harvested for use as nitrate in the manufacture of explosives during the Civil War, and for many years provided nitrates for fertilizer.

Perhaps the cruelest use of bats in history occurred during the Second World War. Small bombs were attached to *Tadarida* bats, which were dropped from planes into enemy territory. The bombs had delayed timing devices on them, which exploded after the bats had settled in villages.

Free-tailed bats have very narrow wings, which beat faster than the wings of most other insect-eating bats. The resulting flight is relatively straight, swift, and usually high, especially during migration. At least one species is known to fly with the mouth open to capture beetles, moths, and other insects.

Free-tailed bat, 8–20 grams

American Leaf-nosed Bats

Big-eared Bat, Macrotus sp.
Wrinkle-faced Bat, Centurio senex

The wrinkle-faced bat, *Centurio senex*, and the three species of big-eared bats (genus *Macrotus*) belong to the large family of American leaf-nosed bats, Phyllostomidae; only the *Macrotus* species, however, exhibit a true leaf nose. The erect "leaf" is triangular, and the muzzle structure is less elaborate than that of Old World leaf-nosed bats.

Big-eared bats eat fruit and insects, the latter caught in flight. They roost in small groups, hanging upside-down in underground caverns. Females congregate to form maternity colonies, where they bear and nurse their single young communally. *Macrotus* bats are found in the southwestern United States south to Guatemala, and in the Bahamas and Greater Antilles.

The wrinkle-faced bat has a unique skin fold that covers the face while the bat roosts; when it flies, the fold is housed as chin wrinkles. The male has additional chin folds that are not part of the mask, but probably contain scent glands. This bat eats fruit primarily. Its throat opening is tiny, and the bat is thought to process the fruit by straining it through nipplelike projections between the lips and gum. *Centurio senex* roosts in small groups in trees from Mexico to Costa Rica and on Trinidad and Tobago.

▲ Wrinkle-faced bat, 15–30 grams
Big-eared bat, 10–20 grams ▶

Common Vampire Bat

Desmodus rotundus

The blood diet of vampire bats has attained legendary proportions, and anyone who has seen a victim knows why. Blood seems to be smeared everywhere. This is not because the size of the bite itself is frighteningly large, but because the bat's saliva contains anticoagulants. The actual wound is only 4 or 5 millimeters wide, and the blood loss is usually not significant. In fact, a bite from the sharp V-shaped canines rarely even disturbs the resting vertebrates on which these bats prey. The real danger is from infection of the wound and the transmission of rabies and other diseases and even parasites.

In addition to flying, vampire bats are able to hop, run, and walk, and so can approach their warm-blooded victims in a variety of ways. They usually feed for a half hour or so, sometime between sunset and midnight, during which time they may consume so much blood that they bloat themselves.

The three genera of true vampire bats contain a single species each. These mammals are found exclusively in the tropics and subtropics of the Americas, where they are thought to breed throughout the year.

Common vampire bat, 15–50 grams

Western Pipistrelle, or Canyon Bat

Pipistrellus hesperus

This tiny desert dweller, with a wingspread of only 190–215 millimeters, is by far the smallest bat in the United States. Though it generally flies early in the evening, it is sometimes seen at midday in cooler areas. In regions with cliffs or outcroppings, roosts often include rock crevices. In the hottest parts of its range (southeastern Washington state to southern Mexico), this pipistrelle probably retreats underground, although no one knows for sure where it goes—perhaps to kangaroo rat burrows.

Pipistrellus hesperus eats insects exclusively and sometimes competes with violet-green swallows and other birds for food. The ear tragus, an external projection located at the base of the ear, is distinctively club-shaped in this species. The tragus's function is to focus more finely the echoes that bounce back to the bat during echolocation. This comparatively large tragus, along with a rather simple nose, distinguishes members of the family Vespertilionidae.

Altogether about forty species of pipistrelles range throughout most of the world exclusive of South America.

Lump-nosed Bat

Plecotus sp.

Lump-nosed bats share an important characteristic with hummingbirds: they hover. They are therefore able to pick moths off walls and foliage, although these bats hunt during regular flight as well. They fly only after dark, usually very slowly.

Large glandular muzzle protrusions give this bat its common name. In some species the protrusions extend above the muzzle as prominent flaplike lumps. In other species flaps between the ears are the most prominent feature.

All five *Plecotus* species hibernate, usually singly. They tuck the long ears under their wings or against their heads when they rest. Roosts include caves, trees, buildings, and tunnels. Some species move from one to another of these roosts according to the season.

Plecotus bats range throughout most of the temperate portions of the world, but are not found in South America.

43

▲ Lump-nosed bat, 5–20 grams
◄ Western pipistrelle, 4–10 grams

Primates

The Primate order includes both human beings and our closest relatives. Order members have developed into quite a variety of forms since their emergence some seventy million years ago. Prosimians are the very rudimentary primates found today in Madagascar and Southeast Asia. They are subdivided into the tree shrews, the lemurs, the lorises, and the tarsiers. Many of them walk with the head held down for sniffing, and their sense of touch is concentrated in the hairs on their pointed muzzles. Unlike the more advanced primates, they mature quickly, most are nocturnal, and they form no complex social units. Births are usually multiple.

As prosimians evolved into more advanced forms, their claws were gradually replaced by digits with nails. Suited for grasping, these allowed the primates to move freely among the branches of trees, where a whole new choice of foods was at their disposal. Millennia of eating from both the treetops and the ground led to a relatively large body size. These adaptations, plus the evolution of a brain with a relatively large area devoted to stereoscopic vision, characterize the higher primates—intelligent, well-sighted animals that hold their heads upright and have versatile grasping appendages.

Today primates are spoken of in terms of where they live. The so-called Old World monkeys inhabit most of Africa and Asia. These include several subgroups: the baboons and macaques, the colobuses and langurs, and the guenons and mangabeys. These primates are characterized by their downward-pointing noses with generally comma-shaped nostrils. None of the Old World monkeys have prehensile tails. They do have, on their buttocks, areas

Senegal bush baby, 230 grams (females), 300 grams (males)

of hardened skin known as ischial callosities, which serve as pads for sitting. Sexual dimorphism, or a pronounced difference (in size, coloration, or structure) between males and females of the same species, is common in the Old World monkeys, especially in those who dwell in open country, where the much larger male's defense of the females and young is essential.

New World monkeys are found exclusively in Central and South America. The marmosets and tamarins are grouped in one family, and all the other New World monkeys in a second, more varied family. All New World monkeys have tails, and many of them have prehensile tails, an adaptation important to such arboreal species. Because they live off the ground where few predators can reach them, there is little need for male protection—hence little difference, in size or strength, between the sexes.

The anthropoid, or manlike, apes live in parts of the Orient and in Africa. They are divided into two families. The Hylobatidae contains the gibbons and related forms, often referred to as the lesser apes. The Pongidae contains the great apes, man's closest living relatives and the largest nonhuman primates.

Senegal Bush Baby

Galago senegalensis

The galagos' loud, wailing cry, like that of a human infant, gives them their common name. They move over level ground by hopping like kangaroos, and sometimes leap three or four meters into the air, seeming to fly among the treetops.

Grooming is carried out with the help of a protuberance under the tongue. Fur is cleaned as it is passed through the front teeth; the under-tongue keeps the grooming "tools" clean by eliminating foreign material collected by the teeth.

The fingers work together, not independently like human fingers; yet the hand can grasp fruits, grasshoppers, and other foods, and hold objects for close inspection. Galagos sometimes moisten their extremities with their own urine, probably to increase their gripping power and to mark territories.

Nocturnal, rather gentle animals, the four species of bush babies inhabit most of Africa south of the Sahara.

Slow loris, 500 grams–1.5 kg

Slow Loris

Nycticebus coucang

Loris, derived from the Dutch word for "clown," is an apt name for this slow-moving, wide-eyed creature. This primate never leaps, but travels in a deliberate hand-over-hand manner along the tops and undersides of branches, much like a sloth. In fact, it fills an ecological niche similar to the South American sloth's.

The slow loris can hold a position almost indefinitely, since its hands and feet actually lock onto branches. The thumbs and toes of its strong extremities are set at right angles to the other digits. The second digit on the hind foot bears a curved claw, used for scratching, and the index digit is very short.

Almost totally arboreal, the slow loris inhabits parts of Southeast Asia, where it eats insects, fruits, stems, leaves, and small mammals, often while hanging from a branch. During the day, when it sleeps, it rolls itself into a ball, perhaps to conserve heat in the absence of a tail to wrap around the body for insulation. Like its movements, the slow loris's metabolism is very sluggish, and the animal would probably die from cold, even in the tropics, if shorn of its coat.

Tree Shrew

Tupaia sp.

Tree shrews were once classified with ground shrews as insectivores. Now, however, they are considered primates, because they have the superior vision and large cerebral cortex (a portion of the brain) characteristic of the order.

Extremely curious, tree shrews will poke their long noses into almost anything, and will eat nearly every kind of food. Insects are pounced upon and killed with the teeth. But fruit is held rather delicately in the hands as a squirrel would hold it, and in fact, the word *Tupaia* comes from a Malay word for "squirrel."

These primates have several different calls, from a pleased whistle to chirps and grunts of alarm. They groom themselves with their lower incisors, except when the females are in heat. Then they behave more like monkeys, and groom each other. When they sleep (in nests of leaves and grasses), they curl their tails around them, holding the ends above their heads. A bothersome insect triggers vigorous tail-waving, yet never seems to disturb a tree shrew's repose.

About ten species are scattered widely throughout the Orient. So far as is known, they breed throughout the year, and usually **48** bear two young per litter.

▲ Tree shrew, 100–180 grams
Black lemur, 2 kg ▶

Black Lemur

Lemur macaco

Madagascar's lush vegetation and warm climate have helped to make that island a haven for lemurs. One theory suggests that a land bridge between Madagascar and the African mainland disappeared some fifty million years ago, separating the early lemurs from competing monkeys (who remained on the mainland). Whatever it was that allowed them to thrive, the lemurs have evolved into a wonderful and varied array of modern primates.

Although the lemurs are more highly evolved than the early prosimians, they are not quite monkeys. They have eyes in front of their heads instead of at the sides, and are considered among the first animals with stereoscopic vision. No doubt the lemurs' agility is enhanced by their depth perception.

The male black lemur usually has soft black fur, the female brown; both sexes have pronounced neck ruffs. Like other prosimians, they have specialized grooming tools—comblike lower incisors and clawlike second toes. Greetings between black lemurs are very ceremonious, with reciprocal fur grooming being the standard procedure. In the treetops, an individual will rub its palms on leaves, branches, and fruits to leave an identifying odor. It also screams to denote territories.

Mindanao Tarsier

Tarsius syrichta

Beguiling animals, tarsiers are the most advanced of the so-called lower primates, those primates from which the monkeys and apes evolved. Their brains are hard to distinguish from those of monkeys, since the parts of the brain that control balance and vision are highly developed in both animals. The tarsier's small nose is in marked contrast to the long snouts of the prosimians and early primates, and reflects the lessened dependence on the sense of smell.

Tarsiers can rotate their heads almost 360 degrees, and so have an extremely wide field of vision, which helps them as they navigate their powerful leaps (often to 150 centimeters). They cling to smooth surfaces with the suction pads on their fingers and toes, and they use their tails as woodpeckers do, for support on vertical tree trunks. The name tarsier refers to the very long ankle, or tarsal, region of the hind legs.

Three species of tarsiers inhabit forests in Indonesia and the **50** Philippines. They feed on lizards, insects, and small birds.

▲ Mindanao tarsier, 80–150 grams
Proboscis monkey, 8–12 kg (females), 15–25 kg (males) ▶

Proboscis Monkey

Nasalis larvatus

Found only on Borneo, the proboscis monkey is distinguished by the huge bulbous nose of the sexually mature male (a male over seven years old). The female, who has a much less obvious snub nose, has a cry reminiscent of a goose's; the male's cry, which he sounds to warn troupe mates of danger, is much deeper and more drawn out. With each "honk" his nose becomes straight and rigid, and by the time a male is very old his nose is so large that it actually gets in the way of eating.

Interestingly, the proboscis monkey is called *orang blanda,* or "white person," by the natives of Borneo. The name most likely refers to the Dutch colonials who settled on the island in the nineteenth century. To the natives their noses seemed so red and enlarged (presumably from drinking) that comparison of them with the proboscis monkey's nose was inevitable.

The proboscis monkey is a leaf-eater, like all the other Old World monkeys known as langurs. It lives in fresh-water deltas and mangrove swamps, where it swims with ease and apparent pleasure and dives exceptionally well.

For reasons that are not entirely clear, the proboscis monkey has rarely been kept successfully in captivity.

Baboons

Chacma, *Papio ursinus*
Yellow Baboon, *Papio cynocephalus*

Baboons live in hierarchical societies that are almost as highly structured as man's. They have a wide range of gestures, including kissing, grooming, and presenting—exposing the rump. Presenting is a mark of respect often directed toward the dominant male in a group.

The vast majority of baboons belong to one of the four species of savannah, or common, baboons—the chacma, the anubis, the yellow baboon, and the olive baboon. They are found in overlapping ranges throughout most of central and southern Africa, wherever there are steppes, savannah, forests, or mountains. Some trees are necessary to baboons, since they provide escape routes as well as sleeping places.

Unlike most wild animals, baboons are not intimidated by human settlements, and in fact rely on crops for much of their food. Where their chief predators, leopards, have been exterminated, baboons have become a serious threat to agriculture.

▲ Chacma, 15–40 kg
Yellow baboon, 15–40 kg ▶

Mandrill, *Papio sphinx*

An agitated male mandrill is unsurpassed in facial coloring, his sky-blue and deep red markings flushing even deeper with increasing excitement. From the rear he is almost as striking: the genitals and buttocks are violet and scarlet.

The hefty older males are the undisputed leaders of their social units, troupes that may number in the forties or fifties. They often wander ahead of their groups, to scout out danger and to ward off adversaries with growls and with yawning gestures that bare the ferocious-looking teeth. Enraged, they can be quite fierce.

The mandrill, along with the related but less spectacular-looking drill, inhabits the forest floor of West Africa near the equator. It probably sleeps in trees. It will eat practically anything, and is itself often eaten as a delicacy by natives of the area. **53**

Mandrill, 40–55 kg

New World Monkeys

Spider Monkey, *Ateles sp.*
Red-faced Ukari, *Cacajao rubicundus*

Two families—the Cebidae and the Callithricidae—make up the entire population of New World primates. The members of both are considered monkeys or monkey allies, neither prosimians nor apes being found outside the Old World.

The four spider monkey species have the most dexterous prehensile tail of all New World monkeys. The underside of the long tail is hairless at the tip, with ridges that provide a strong grip as well as delicate feeling. Spider monkeys have the round, wide-set nostrils that give New World monkeys the scientific name Platyrrhini, "broad-nosed." They inhabit tropical forests from southern Mexico to central Bolivia and into Brazil.

The three ukari species inhabit three distinct areas along the Amazonian rivers. They are the only short-tailed New World monkeys, and thus are among the few New World monkeys without prehensile tails. The red-faced ukari has rosy skin that flushes to scarlet when it is agitated. It can leap, but usually moves slowly on all fours. It rarely descends to the ground.

▲ Red-faced ukari, 2.9–4.4 kg
Spider monkey, 6 kg ▶

Golden Marmoset, *Leontideus rosalia*

Among the smaller primates, marmosets usually weigh under 1,000 grams and are extremely agile. They have no nails on their extremities, and they climb like squirrels, by gripping with their claws. Definite ear tufts distinguish them from their close relatives the tamarins.

The male golden marmoset is unusually solicitous of its off-spring (most often twins): it helps with their transportation; it gives the very young to the mother for feeding; and it handles solid food (fruit, insects, and some small reptiles and birds) to break it down and make it digestible to the newly weaned. By the time they are a year old, the twins are considered adults, and can care for themselves.

Unfortunately, only a few hundred golden marmosets still survive in the forests of eastern Brazil. Since members of this genus do not adapt to cultivated land, and since Brazil is quickly eradicating many of her native forests, the future of these primates seems bleak indeed.

55

Golden marmoset, 350–500 grams

Lar Gibbon

Hylobates lar

Gibbons are the trapeze artists of the primate world. Their lovely slender bodies swing along on very long arms, through the trees of Indonesia and Indochina. They are propelled by a rapid hand-over-hand type of locomotion called brachiation, and can easily cover 3 meters in a single swing. When on the ground gibbons walk and run upright, using their arms for balancing; they do not swim.

Their voices are lyrical, and they repeat the sound *oo-ah* on an ascending, then a descending, scale at mate-calling time.

Figs and other fruits, birds' eggs, and ants figure in the gibbon's diet, and are usually consumed rather delicately, the skins being removed from fruits along with any small imperfections.

The lar gibbon has at least two color phases, buff and black. In both, the fur around the face is white, as are the backs of the hands and feet—thus the nickname white-handed gibbon.

▲ Lar gibbon, 5–8 kg
Orangutan, 40 kg (females), 75–100 kg (males) ▶

Orangutan

Pongo pygmaeus

The orangutan stands out among nonhuman primates because most of the adults of the species are solitary. A mother and her offspring are an exception: a young orangutan clings to its mother's body almost continually for its first eighteen months, and sometimes remains in her company for three to four years. During this time the mother engages in no sexual activity, and so produces relatively few young during her lifetime.

The orangutan is rather poorly equipped to move about on the ground, but it uses its agile limbs to climb slowly in the trees, where it sleeps in a different nest each night. During the day it may wait out a rainstorm under an "umbrella" it makes from leaves and branches. It eats fruits such as the durian, mangosteen, and rambutan, along with various shoots. The rarest of the apes, the orangutan is found today only in the tropical forests of Borneo and Sumatra, where no more than five thousand are thought to survive. Local conservation groups are trying hard to insure their preservation.

Gorilla

Gorilla gorilla

"Introverted, peaceful vegetarians," the description of gorillas given by a recent close observer in the wild, seems heretical when contrasted with earlier, fiercer accounts of these anthropoids' behavior. Gorillas start their day by feeding heartily on bamboo, nettles, roots, and bark. After a siesta and a sunning, a troupe of six to ten females with young will follow their leader, usually a silver-backed male, half a mile or so to that night's nesting spot. Another meal is followed by nest-building and then sleep.

Although these nomads are not territorial in the usual sense, the dominant male will beat his chest to alert other troupes to his presence. If further communication is necessary, he may hoot, run, or tear at vegetation. But for the most part, he is gentle with other males. He tolerates little scrapping among his troupe, however, and may discipline offenders with piglike grunts. When contented, gorillas will belch; when curious, they bark.

Lowland gorillas inhabit western Africa; mountain gorillas **58** are found in central and eastern Africa.

Gorilla, 135–200 kg (females), 180–275 kg (males)

Chimpanzee

Chimpansee troglodytes

Chimpanzees, gorillas, and orangutans are known as the great apes, gibbons and siamangs as the lesser apes. The two groups together make up the anthropoids, primates that began to evolve different traits from monkeys some 24 million years ago.

Anthropoids have much more complex emotional and social responses than monkeys. They also have longer periods of infancy, youth, and adolescence, and thus more time for learning. Apes have longer arms and shorter trunks than monkeys, as well as shorter lumbar regions.

Of all the anthropoids, the chimpanzee is the most intelligent. It learns at about the same rate as a human infant until it is a year old, and its communication systems are far richer than any other nonhuman primate's. In the wild, chimpanzees live in groups of twenty-five to seventy-five. Subgroups develop within each troupe, a mother and a single infant being the most stable unit. Males seem to gain and lose dominance quickly and often, and have no specific mates. Chimpanzees inhabit the forests of central Africa.

Chimpanzee, 45–70 kg (females), 55–80 kg (males)

Edentata

"Edentata" means "lacking teeth," but except for the anteaters, all members of this order have some teeth. What they lack are canines and incisors, the teeth most mammals use in self-defense and in eating. Edentates use their claws as weapons, and many of them capture insects and other foods with their sticky tongues.

Edentates, varied in habit and appearance, include the sloths, anteaters, and armadillos. Thought to be a New World order, they are found mainly in Central and South America.

Two-toed Sloth

Choloepus sp.

Despite their bad reputation, sloths are neither lazy nor slovenly. They sleep up to fifteen hours a day, but this is due to a small heart and a slow metabolism. In the treetops they move in a deliberate, hand-over-hand fashion, and on the ground they pull their bodies up behind them by grabbing claw-holds. They are simply not built to stand. In the trees, their hooklike "fingers" allow them to hang upside-down easily, and they carry out most activities in this position. Sloths swim well, and they sleep with their head tucked between their forelegs.

These are among the few mammals with imperfectly regulated warm-bloodedness—their body temperature fluctuates about 10° C. As a result, they are not easily taken from their constantly warm range (Honduras and south throughout most of South America). Sloths are a strange sight during the rainy season: they take on the green tinge of the algae they host. Appearing to smile perpetually, they can turn their heads in a 270-degree arc.

Two-toed sloth, 9 kg

Nine-banded Armadillo

Dasypus novemcinctus

The nine-banded armadillo takes its name from the girdle of bands surrounding its midsection. (Actually, in the five species of nine-banded armadillos, the number of bands varies from seven to ten.) The bands afford this otherwise stiffly armored mammal some degree of flexibility, allowing it to curl into an impenetrable ball when threatened. It does not depend totally on this one defense tactic, however, since it often escapes danger by retreating to a burrow, going into a thicket, or quickly digging itself into the ground.

Armadillos are almost blind, and have been known to bump into people's legs during their nighttime forays. Their sense of smell leads them to insect burrows, where they feed on grasshoppers, roaches, and other potential pests. They sometimes eat scorpions and tarantulas. They generally feed in groups, grunting almost continually as they do so.

These mammals cross small bodies of water simply by walking across the bottom. When they must swim large rivers, they swallow enough air to inflate their intestinal tract, which then keeps them afloat.

Within the past century, nine-banded armadillos have extended their range northward into North America from as far south as Colombia.

Giant Anteater

Myrmecophaga tridactyla

Three anteater species exist—the giant, the least, and the collared. They are the only living mammals with no teeth of any kind. They capture their food on their long sticky tongues, after their strong foreclaws have demolished an ants' nest or a termite mound. The giant anteater supplements its diet with beetle larvae. Its slender head is well shaped for probing.

By shuffling along on its knuckles, the giant anteater protects its valuable claws, which it uses for self-defense as well as for demolition. It can gallop, and it swims well and seems to enjoy the water. Some authorities claim that the giant anteater uses its bushy tail as a broom and as a sunshade.

The female giant anteater bears a single offspring, who rides piggyback on its mother, often until she mates again. Otherwise, this mammal is solitary throughout its range, tropical forests and savannahs from Belize to Paraguay and northern Argentina. It does not burrow, but takes shelter under bushes and in other protected spots.

63

▲ Giant anteater, 18–25 kg
◄ Nine-banded armadillo, 4–8 kg

Pholidota

The order Pholidota (the word means "covered with scales") contains a single genus and seven species, all of them commonly known as pangolins or scaly anteaters.

Three species inhabit Asia and parts of Southeast Asia, and four inhabit equatorial Africa. The Asian species have several hairs growing at the base of each scale, as well as some kind of projecting ear part. Both of these features are absent in African pangolins.

African Tree Pangolin

Manis tricuspis

Pangolins have astonishing tongues—they are so long that they are actually anchored in the animal's pelvic region. After the strong foreclaws have ripped open a termites' or an ants' nest, the tongue shoots out and, with adhesive saliva, captures the insects. Ears and nostrils close and so become impervious to swarming ants or termites.

The sharp scales that cover the upper parts of this mammal's body are more or less fan-shaped. A threatened pangolin will roll itself into a spiral, with the scales on the outside and the softer body parts in the center. When in this position it twitches its scales, which are movable, to dispel enemies. Persistent predators who try to pry open the scaly ball almost always fail. A foul-smelling liquid is sometimes ejected from the pangolin's anal region as a further defense.

Scaly anteaters are solitary most of the time. They walk on their hind legs, using their tails as a brace, or on all fours, on their knuckles. They use their foreclaws to dig burrows, into which annual litters of one or two young are born.

65

African tree pangolin, 5–25 kg

Lagomorpha

Lagomorphs used to be classified with the rodents. Due to anatomical and dental differences, however, they are now classified separately. Lagomorphs have two pairs of upper incisors, whereas rodents have only 'one. Lagomorphs' jaws can move sideways in chewing, and they eat their moist fecal pellets but not their dry ones.

Two families make up this order—the Ochotonidae, which contains the pikas, and the Leporidae, which contains the fifty or so species of rabbits and hares.

Pika

Ochotona sp.

Pikas are hard to miss—their bleating squeaks, which they project like ventriloquists, give them away. The two New World species inhabit talus slopes and rockslides in western North America, and the twelve Old World species live in various habitats throughout most of Asia.

These mammals differ from rabbits and hares in the uniform length of their limbs, their inability to hop or sit up, and their basically diurnal habits. They are adapted to year-round activity by their practice of drying vegetation in the sun, then piling it up to eat later. These "haystacks" save the pika's life in winter, for it is not equipped to forage widely in the snow. They also serve as resting spots, and become scattered with tiny droppings that resemble rabbit pellets.

Also called rock conies, New World pikas produce few offspring for a lagomorph, only three or four a year. However, they are able to maintain fairly stable populations, since they vanish into cracks and crevices among the rocks so quickly that few predators can catch them. **67**

Pika, 100–125 grams

Snowshoe, or Varying, Hare

Lepus americanus

The broad surface of the snowshoe hare's hind foot gives the animal its name and affords it maneuverability and speed in the snow. Long, bristly hairs, which grow about the toes and the side of the foot in autumn, provide insulation from the snow. As with jackrabbits and cottontails, the snowshoe hare's hind foot prints ahead of the front foot, leaving a trail that is easy to spot.

The snowshoe hare is also called the varying hare, because its coat changes dramatically with the seasons. White during the six months of northern North America's winter, the fur turns to brown in the spring. Most probably this molt is regulated by the amount of daylight that strikes the hare's eyes—reduced light (in autumn and winter) lessens the production of brown pigment, and vice versa in the spring and summer.

Unlike many rabbits, hares dig no burrows, but live and raise their offspring (which are fully furred at birth) entirely above-ground. Although prolific—three or four litters of several young each are born every year—a number of factors, including disease, parasites, and starvation, help keep populations in check. In addition, the snowshoe hare experiences a population peak, followed by a dramatic crash, about once every ten years. Prey populations, particularly the lynx's, have parallel fluctuations. The exact reasons for these cycles are unknown.

Old World Rabbit

Oryctolagus cuniculus

Common, or Old World, rabbits are probably the best-known lagomorphs. They are extremely gregarious, often living in groups of up to 150 individuals. They dig burrows and set up nesting areas within them, which they carefully line with vegetation and with fur that the mother rabbit takes from her own soft underparts. After a gestation period of about a month, three to eight blind, naked young are born. The female can mate again within twelve to fifteen hours after giving birth. Theoretically, as many as six litters can be produced within one mating season, usually January to June. However, the frequency of spontaneous abortion and embryo reabsorption is extremely high.

These rabbits are native to northwestern Africa and southwestern Europe. They have been introduced into many other regions, where their populations have often reached pest proportions due to the absence of natural predators. Introduction of the Old World rabbit into Australia, for example, has had only the direst of consequences—the rapid depletion of huge amounts of vegetation.

▲ Old World rabbit, 1.3–2.25 kg
◀ Snowshoe hare, 1.3–7 kg

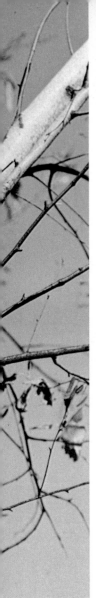

Rodentia

Rodents are by far the largest order of mammals—6,400 species in all. This is more than half the total number of mammal species!

All rodents have four incisors, two upper and two lower, which determine their life style: the teeth grow continually and would incapacitate a rodent's mouth if constant gnawing did not keep them worn down. The tooth's enamel-covered outer surface is very hard and forms a sharp cutting edge as the softer underparts wear down.

Except for *Homo sapiens* and possibly some hares, moles, and carnivores, rodents are the only animals that habitually store food (mostly herbaceous) for later use. Often they excavate burrows with their incisors. Inveterate home-makers, rodents are nest-builders, and may shred or otherwise process their nesting materials before they use them. These relatively small creatures have a high birth rate, which insures survival of a species in spite of its many predators. They are found in various habitats throughout most of the world.

Human beings cannot ignore rodents, since they transmit many diseases and destroy many crops. At the same time, mice and rats are valuable research tools; beavers build dams that benefit wildlife by providing a year-round water supply; and other rodents keep harmful insects and weeds in check. Unlike many other mammals, rodents seem to thrive in the face of man's encroaching civilization.

Three rodent suborders are recognized today. The Sciuromorpha, or squirrellike rodents, evolved the earliest, and from them evolved the Myomorpha, or mouselike rodents, and the Hystricomorpha, or porcupinelike rodents.

North American porcupine, 3.5–15 kg

North American Porcupine

Erethizon dorsatum

This slow-moving New World species has feet specialized for arboreal living, a feature not shared by Old World counterparts such as the brush-tailed porcupines. Found in most of wooded North America, the porcupine is somewhat awkward on the ground, but its hollow, barbed quills give this animal the buoyancy to swim well. The quills, loosely attached to the porcupine's body and tail, are brushed against menacing predators such as bobcats or fishers. They take hold at once and can easily work themselves into the enemy's muscles and vital organs. The porcupine often chatters its teeth when threatened, and keeps its arched back turned toward its foe.

This mammal has very poor eyesight, but a keen sense of smell. On occasion it performs a unique "dance," the purpose of which is not understood, in which it shifts its weight from one hind foot to the other with accompanying forefoot and head movements. The porcupine eats tree bark in winter, and tender young buds, leaves, and twigs when available.

The female porcupine bears her single offspring six to seven months after an autumn mating. The newborn's quills are soft and covered with a membrane at birth, and harden within approximately thirty minutes.

Chipmunks

Eastern Chipmunk, *Tamias striatus*
Western Chipmunk, *Eutamias sp.*

Chipmunks seem to triple the size of their heads when they stuff their cheek pouches with nuts and other foods that they store away for winter. Since they do not really hibernate, they may arise from their torpid state to feast at any time. In this way they differ from the ground squirrels, which burn body fat during their dormant periods.

The single species of eastern American chipmunk has red-tinged hindquarters. It is a quick and playful mammal, often tamed for a pet. These chipmunks inhabit populated areas

throughout the eastern United States and southeastern Canada

and are frequently seen scampering along the edges of woods in search of small fruits, corn, and other warm-weather foods.

The Siberian chipmunk is closely related to the seventeen species of North American western chipmunks. The former inhabits much of Asia, the latter occupy a wide variety of habitats, as they range from the Yukon Territory to Baja California and northern Mexico. Smaller than the eastern species, western chipmunks have longer tails, and their longitudinal stripes (five black, four white) are more pronounced.

73

Top: Western chipmunk, 25–125 grams
Bottom: Eastern chipmunk, 70–145 grams

Eurasian Tree Squirrel

Sciurus vulgaris

Eurasian tree squirrels, particularly the females, seem to be compulsive nest-builders. After making several auxiliary nests, to be used in emergencies, they begin work on the principal nest, which may be under construction for anywhere from three to five days. Usually located in the forks of trees, the nests are made of twigs and branches which are interwoven from the bottom up and then lined with lichens, mosses, bark, and dried leaves. In addition, a few unlined nests give protection from the sun and from predators, and provide the squirrels with a safe place to eat. These squirrels seldom leave their evergreen trees except to forage, usually for scent-marked nuts and seeds that have been buried individually, or ''scatter-hoarded.''

Sciurus vulgaris has conspicuous ear tufts, and it molts twice a year. The coat is usually rust or black in summer and gray in winter, when a rust stripe may be present along the spine. When alarmed, this squirrel ''barks'' and shakes its tail vigorously.

The Eurasian tree squirrel ranges widely over most of Europe and Asia, including Russia. The gestation period is about thirty-eight days, and two litters of five to seven young each are produced every year.

Eurasian tree squirrel, 200–900 grams

Eastern Red Squirrel

Tamiasciurus hudsonicus

Red squirrels are the real "characters" of the squirrel tribe. They scold, fuss, and chatter noisily, and in fact are usually heard before they are seen in the woods. Several piles of seed husks and discarded evergreen cones indicate their favorite eating spots. These small squirrels do not scatter-hoard, but store large quantities of cones clipped from spruce and other trees. They jealously guard their caches and their territories year-round and do not hibernate. Abandoned woodpecker holes and hollow trees provide nesting places and shelter from birds of prey, martens, and other red squirrel enemies.

Two species of red squirrels are generally recognized. *Tamiasciurus hudsonicus,* which is by far the more abundant, inhabits forests throughout most of Canada and into the United States in Idaho, Montana, Wyoming, and the northeastern states. This species has definite white underparts, which are lacking in *T. douglassi.* This latter species ranges west of the Rockies, and is sometimes called the chickaree.

In some North American locales, populations of gray squirrels (close cousins of the red squirrels) have been fed by people so regularly that they have become almost tame.

Eastern red squirrel, 140–315 grams

African Ground Squirrel

Xerus sp.

Rarely do human beings have the chance to witness the development of an adaptation. Some of the African ground squirrels, however, have given us the opportunity to so do. As Africa has eradicated many of its forests, some squirrels have had to learn to live on the ground, and the *Xerus* species are among these. A similar pattern has occurred in portions of the United States, where conifers have been burned over and the new growth has not had time to mature fully. Lacking the cavities of old hollow trees in which to nest, some "flying" squirrels have taken to holes in the ground.

One of the two *Xerus* species constructs towns similar to those of the prairie dog, its close cousin. Since they are not intimidated by human beings, ground squirrels of the genus *Xerus* are well known throughout their ranges. *X. rutilus* inhabits the northeastern part of Africa, and the other species, *X. erythropus*, inhabits the eastern and western parts of the continent. The genus *Geosciurus,* which inhabits southern and western Africa, is sometimes considered a subgenus of *Xerus*.

African ground squirrel, 620–720 grams

Golden-mantled Ground Squirrel

Callospermophilus lateralis

Graveled slopes in North America's western mountains host this handsome ground squirrel, and many a tourist in the national parks has helped to fatten it for hibernation. The golden-mantled ground squirrel hibernates restlessly, for about seven months of the year, in a rather unkempt burrow more than 3 meters long. Midway between the burrow's front and back entrances is the den, with its nest of dried vegetation made bulky for winter use. Early spring brings the squirrels from their solitary dwellings. They mate soon after, and a litter of five or six young is born about a month later. After a summer of eating grasses, piñon pine cones, mushrooms, gooseberries, and whatever other foods they can find or beg, they settle in for another long sleep.

Golden-mantled ground squirrels are twice as large as the western chipmunks, which they resemble except in facial patterning. They have rather scrappy and insignificant fights among themselves, in which they roll over and over to a whole repertoire of chirps, buzzes, screams, and grunts. When simply nervous, they flick their tails and make a *tkk-tkk* sound.

Golden-mantled ground squirrel, 175–275 grams

Asiatic Striped Palm Squirrel

Funambulus sp.

Nectar from the silky oak is irresistible to Asiatic striped palm squirrels. They become covered with pollen in obtaining it, and so are important to the process of pollination. Cocoa pods and parts of the silk cotton tree (from which kapok is produced) make up the balance of their diet, along with the usual seeds, bark, and leaves.

Five species of this palm squirrel inhabit India, Ceylon, and southwestern Pakistan. All five have three distinct stripes running the length of the back. They differ in their habitats, some preferring densely wooded areas, others more open scrub growth. As far as is known, none is strictly terrestrial or arboreal.

Like most rodents, these squirrels cannot be said to "display," or perform some action that will attract a member of the opposite sex during mating season. However, fights among several rival males are common. The female bears her three or four offspring in a spherical nest in the trees, and refuses male contact for about two months thereafter, until the young are **78** weaned.

Asiatic striped palm squirrels, 90–125 grams

Old World Flying Squirrel

Pteromys volans

Flying squirrels do not fly, they glide, held aloft by a patagium, a furred membrane similar to that of a bat. In members of the genus *Pteromys* the patagium extends from wrist to ankle; in members of the genus *Petaurista* it continues on to the base of the tail. When the squirrel extends its limbs the patagium spreads to become a parachute.

A noiseless glide of 40 meters is not uncommon for flying squirrels. Though they usually glide downward in straight lines, they can shift direction in mid-flight and even use thermals to help them swing upward. Flying squirrels always land on the trunks of trees rather than in the branches. When at rest they fold their gliding membranes under them.

The Old World flying squirrel ranges from southeastern Scandinavia east throughout most of northern Europe and Asia, and along the Pacific coast south to Japan. It shelters in hollow evergreen trees or in nests of lichens and moss, which it rarely if ever leaves during the day. Seeds, buds, bark, and some fruit make up its diet.

79

Old World flying squirrel, 170–285 grams

Woodchuck

Marmota monax

Among the few true hibernators, the woodchuck (also known as the ground hog) sleeps in its multichambered burrow from late fall until the beginning of February. Its body processes slowed dramatically, it subsists on stored fat, having gorged itself on green vegetation the preceding summer. On February 2, Ground Hog Day, it emerges: according to legend, if it sees its shadow, there will be six more weeks of winter.

The woodchuck's piercing whistle can be heard in woodlands and fields throughout the eastern United States and most of Canada. In all but the northernmost parts of this range, mating occurs in the early spring. After a gestation period of about forty days, between two and nine young are born.

The woodchuck is a close cousin of the yellow-bellied marmot, or rockchuck, of the American West, and of the more northwesterly hoary marmot.

▲ Woodchuck, 3–7.5 kg
Black-tailed prairie dog, 1–1.5 kg ▶

Black-tailed Prairie Dog

Cynomys ludovicianus

Prairie dogs are colonial vegetarians known for their elaborately structured "towns" and the furious "barking" sounds they make when distressed. Once abundant over many acres of North America's prairie, they have been systematically exterminated by ranchers who disliked their competing with livestock for food and land. Now prairie dogs proliferate only in the national parks, and the black-footed ferret, which preys on prairie dogs and nests in their burrows, is almost extinct.

Most prairie dogs surround the entrances to their burrows with dikes of mounded earth, which double as lookout stations. As long as calm prevails, they forage up to 30 meters from home. But when warned of danger by a fellow's whistle or yap, these rodents go scurrying over their mounds and into their tunnels, to take refuge in one of its several subterranean rooms.

Mating occurs once a year, usually around the first of February, and three to six young are born after a gestation period of about thirty days.

Eastern American Pocket Gopher

Geomys sp.

Pocket gophers can gnaw at soil and other inedible substances without getting them in their mouths. This is due to a special adaptation that enables the lips to close in back of the teeth as the gopher burrows. These animals have relatively large fur-lined cheek pouches used for transporting food (roots, bulbs, and stems) to storage places. To clean the pouches, the gopher turns them completely inside out. They return to normal position through the action of a specialized muscle.

These small rodents are pugnacious. Their forefeet, long and clawed, are probably used as weapons in the fights that frequently break out between individuals. (The claws help in burrowing, too.) Pocket gophers hiss when agitated, and they sometimes cry when injured.

About thirty species of pocket gophers inhabit most of North America, wherever the soil is suited for digging. Their tunneling benefits the soil by aerating it. Pocket gophers do not hibernate, but travel in deep snow in the colder parts of their range.

▲ Eastern American pocket gopher, 300–450 grams
Beavers, 10–15 kg ▶

Beaver

Castor canadensis

The beaver is the largest rodent in North America, and except for the capybara, the largest in the world. An excellent swimmer, it uses its flat tail as a rudder, and slaps the water noisily with it in an effort to startle otters and other enemies.

Like all rodents, beavers must gnaw continually to keep their constantly growing incisors worn down. Trees felled as a result of their gnawing are usually cemented with mud into elaborate dams, which can be seen lying across streams throughout most of North America. Ponds created by beaver dams provide caches where winter food such as aspen and willow are anchored in the mud; they also provide a year-round water supply for wildlife. A stout lodge is constructed in the pond, with at least one underwater entrance. Like the dam, it is a mud-plastered structure of sticks and logs.

The fur trade seriously threatened the beaver in the early years of America's development. Now it is protected by law, and rears its one to six annual young in the good graces of forest conservationists and livestock ranchers.

Merriam's Kangaroo Rat

Dipodomys merriami

The dry heat and open, unprotected spaces of the desert are major threats to the Merriam's kangaroo rat. Yet it is adapted to handle both. It avoids high midday temperatures by staying in its burrow until evening. It hardly ever drinks, but manufactures water through the oxidation of carbohydrates in seed plants and other foods. And it excretes very little water in its urine, which has a high concentration of salt and urea. If this rodent does become dangerously overheated, it salivates heavily and then licks its entire body. As the saliva evaporates, cooling occurs.

The Merriam's kangaroo rat stuffs its cheek pouches quickly, then retires to its burrow, where it can eat in safety. Only the short forefeet and cheek pouches are involved in foraging (the eyes being so situated that this kangaroo rat cannot see what it is eating), while only the long hind legs and the eyes are involved in rapid locomotion. This specialization of body parts allows the Merriam's kangaroo rat to stop feeding and begin leaping with no time loss, an adaptation valuable to dwellers of open country, where predators are plentiful.

The tufted tail of this desert animal is longer than its head and body together, and is a marvelous balancing aid. Erratic hopping is this rodent's real trademark, along with the dust-bathing that keeps its body free of foreign particles.

The Merriam's kangaroo rat inhabits various portions of southwestern North America, including Baja California.

Springhare

Pedetes capensis

The springhare resembles a miniature kangaroo. This nocturnal rodent inhabits sandy, dry soil in the more arid portions of east-central Africa. Food is scanty there, and the springhare must forage widely. It may move on all fours like a rabbit, or, if agitated, it may execute leaps of 8 or 9 meters, landing on its huge hind feet. Then the short front feet are held close under the chin, and are all but invisible to onlookers. Steering is no problem, since the tail (curled over the back as the animal hops) allows for balance and a change of direction with each bound. Predators are usually foiled by such dodging tactics, and generally have little luck in catching the wily springhare.

Specialized ear parts close when this animal digs, which it does very rapidly with the curved claws on its front feet. Springhares may dig their burrows close together, but they are essentially solitary creatures and cannot be said to live in true communal warrens. The springhare sleeps in its burrow with its tail wrapped around its curled-up body.

▲ Springhare, 4 kg
◄ Merriam's kangaroo rat, 35–150 grams

Meadow Vole

Microtus pennsylvanicus

The meadow vole is extremely prolific. The female first mates when she is only a month old, and the gestation period is a mere three weeks. Four to eight young are born in each litter, and litters are produced up to seventeen times throughout the year. When the offspring are only a few weeks old and still in their juvenile coats, they leave their spherical nests of dry grasses to establish their own family dwellings. (An average of thirty voles per acre is not uncommon.) Perhaps because it lives in such a seeming rush, the meadow vole's life span is relatively short— rarely more than a year or two.

Also called the field mouse or meadow mouse, *Microtus pennsylvanicus* is the most widely distributed North American vole, inhabiting most of the bogs and grassy areas of the northern United States and Canada. It is active year-round and makes both underground and surface runways in fields where it feeds. Eating its weight in grasses, seeds, and other vegetable matter every day, it would be a serious environmental threat were it not for the many snakes, birds, carnivores, and other animals that prey on it. Occasional plagues also help to control its numbers.

Meadow vole, 85–115 grams

Muskrat

Ondatra zibethica

The living habits of these stocky rodents are somewhat like the beaver's. Muskrats usually construct feeding rafts and mound-shaped lodges in the water, made of cattails, rushes, and sticks, with mud or peat for mortar. Or, if the marshes and rivers they inhabit have steep banks, they may excavate tunnels for homes. In either case, muskrats keep their dwellings extremely clean: they deposit droppings in one of three or four designated places, and they replace moldy bedding with fresh vegetation.

The vertically flattened tail acts as a rudder when the muskrat swims in search of crayfish. Various roots and stems, as well as mussels, are also eaten.

Muskrats are prey to mink and other weasels, as well as to man. Their tender red meat is eaten in some locales; their musk glands, from which the males secrete oil to mark territories, are dried for use in the manufacture of perfume; and more than ten million muskrat pelts are taken annually by the fur industry. Still, muskrats are able to maintain large populations over most of North America and parts of Europe, for they produce litters of four to six young three times a year.

Muskrat, 680 grams–1.8 kg

Norway Rat

Rattus norvegicus

Most cities and farms throughout the world are hosts to rats. During the day several Norway (brown) rats may share a burrow. At night they emerge to scavenge for food among trash piles and litter. They eat enormous quantities of grain, as well as items such as books and building materials, and seem to have a special fondness for the insulation on electrical wiring. They will cut through lead pipes and concrete dams to get the large amounts of water they require. In short, rats are responsible for billions of dollars' worth of damage each year.

Believed to be natives of Asia, Norway rats are notorious disease carriers. Typhus, bubonic plague, rabies, trichinosis, and rat-bite fever are just a few of the diseases they or their parasites transmit. Were it not for their many predators, including birds of prey and numerous carnivores, rats would soon create an even greater problem than they do, since they produce between two and twelve young up to twelve times a year.

Norway rat, 200–500 grams

Brown Lemming

Lemmus trimucronatus

Lemmings, considered a type of mouse by some scientists, respond periodically to crowding and other pressures by emigrating in great hordes from their native tundras (sparsely vegetated Arctic plains). Eating sedges and grasses as they go, they swarm across ridges and other obstacles and swim quiet bodies of water with no hesitation. Many of them are eaten along the way by carnivores and birds of prey, while others simply die of exhaustion or disease. The few individuals who do not emigrate eventually help rebuild the population, which peaks again in three to five years.

The brown lemming inhabits much of Arctic North America. Its emigrations usually last only a few weeks, a short while when compared with the movements of the Scandinavian lemming, whose emigrations may continue for a year or two. In fact, the phrase "like lemmings to the sea" probably refers to Scandinavian lemmings, who often reach the ocean, where they perish in the overwhelming surf.

Another type of lemming, the collared lemming, is unique among mice, since it alone changes its coat in winter. Its brown summer fur gradually becomes streaked with white until it entirely matches the snow. During this season it is almost impossible to distinguish collared lemmings from the albino lemmings common in some areas.

Brown lemming, 40–115 grams

Edible Dormouse

Myoxus glis

The white meat of the edible dormouse has been considered a culinary treat ever since the Romans first began fattening this rodent for consumption. This dormouse is superior to squirrels in its acrobatics, and can somersault through the air, even at night, without mishap. If it tumbles from a tree, it lands on all fours like a cat, making only a quiet squeak as it falls.

Edible dormice build fibrous nests in hollow trees, in gardens, and in abandoned rabbit haunts throughout most of Europe and parts of Asia. Most are dormant up to seven months at a time, rising from their curled-up winter position only occasionally to feed on nuts and seeds. The closely related dormice of the genus *Muscardinus* construct a separate nest for their period of dormancy, along with one for bearing young and another for shelter. The "dormancy nest" is held together with a special secretion from their salivary glands.

Dormice become very noisy at mating time, chirping and whistling loudly. The edible dormouse has a relatively low reproductive rate—it bears only one litter of two to six young a year.

North American Meadow Jumping Mouse

Zapus hudsonius

This jumping mouse is only a little more than 10 centimeters long, excluding the tail. Yet its tiny body (it weighs less than 40 grams) can sail 3.5–4.5 meters in a single bound. Much of this rodent's success in leaping is due to its scantily haired tail, which is twice the length of its body and, with the aid of the huge hind feet, serves as a balance. Drumming the tail on the ground also sends signals to other jumping mice.

Jumping mice of both the *Zapus* (meadow) and *Napaeozapus* (woodland) genera have very nervous temperaments. The meadow jumping mice need little drinking water, since they obtain moisture from dew and from the vegetation they consume. The only obvious difference in the appearance of the two groups is in their tails—black in the *Zapus* mice, white-tipped in the other.

Woodland jumping mice confine themselves to northeastern North America; the meadow-dwelling species span all but the extreme northern and southern parts of the continent. Primarily nocturnal, they are rarely seen throughout their ranges.

▲ North American meadow jumping mouse, 19–37 grams
◄ Edible dormouse, 175 grams

Paca

Agouti paca

The paca has a resonating chamber in its double-pouched cheeks, and produces a rumbling sound as it blows air from the exterior pouches to the interior ones. It is the only mammal that can do this. The false paca, or pacarana, resembles the paca in appearance, but is distinguished from it by its long tail and cranial characteristics.

Like the capybara, and its family members the agoutis, the paca is considered a hystricomorph (a porcupinelike mammal). When it moves, it resembles small ungulates such as the dik-dik. Its forefeet are semiplantigrade, its hind feet semidigitigrade, so that it runs with the heel off the ground. When at rest, it sits or crouches on its haunches.

Ranging from Mexico south through most of Brazil, the paca burrows in banks or takes shelter in tree roots during the day. At dusk it emerges to feed on mangoes, avocados, and various stems and leaves. It usually moves alone through the forest, preferring land to water, but it will swim if it must to escape an enemy. The paca's flesh is considered a delicacy, and the animal is hunted with dogs throughout much of its range.

During courtship mates will squirt each other with urine, a technique also used occasionally in self-defense. The paca bears two litters a year, usually with a single young in each litter.

Pacas, 6–10 kg

Capybara

Hydrochoerus hydrochaeris

The capybara, the world's largest rodent, is a robust mammal whose weight often exceeds 50 kilograms. Its appearance is considered almost ludicrous because of the unusual combination of features: a deep, squared-off jaw, tiny eyes set far back on the head, partly webbed, clawed feet, and a long pelage so sparse that the skin shows through it. On land it resembles the pigs, guinea pigs, and its relatives the cavies; in the water it swims with the ears, eyes, and nose aligned, and so resembles a small hippo. The Latin name means "water hog," which fits the capybara well, for it is found near fresh and brackish waters in South America east of the Andes and south to the River Plate. Water plants and grasses from stream, river, and lake banks make up its diet.

Except where molested by man, capybaras are diurnal, rather placid creatures. They live in herds of three to thirty individuals, and communicate via a wide assortment of clicks, whistles, barks, and grunts. They are prey to jaguars on land, and to alligators in the water. Man hunts them for their skin, kept fatty in the mature males by secretions from large sebaceous glands.

Two species of capybara exist—the larger *hydrochaeris* and the smaller *isthmius* species. The latter inhabits Panama east of the canal and is about half the size of the former. **93**

Capybara, 25–50 kg

Cetacea

Cetaceans are marine mammals —whales, dolphins, and porpoises. They possess large, complex brains, and are profoundly intelligent and sensitive, a fact that human beings are just beginning to comprehend. They engage in extensive play sessions and have unique communication networks through which they register and respond to the smallest details of health and emotion in their fellows.

This order contains the largest animal ever to have lived on earth, the magnificent but endangered blue whale. Whales are able to attain enormous sizes (up to 45 metric tons) because they inhabit a wholly aquatic environment and thus do not have to support their own weight. A layer of blubber just under the skin insulates them from extreme ocean temperatures.

A whale's torpedo-shaped body encounters minimal water resistance. It is propelled by an up-and-down movement of the horizontal tail flukes; the front flippers are used for steering. Some whales migrate enormous distances using this method of locomotion, and they orient themselves and locate food through an echolocation system similar to a bat's. They do not maintain homes in any usual sense.

The cetaceans' need for air is met in various ways. Both their respiratory and circulatory systems maximize available oxygen. Females bear their offspring tail-first, which keeps the young from drowning during birth, before it can reach the surface of the water to breathe. When the newborn touches its mother's nipple, muscles around the mammary gland contract to squirt milk into the offspring's mouth. This provides a lot of milk quickly, so the young whale need not be submerged for long nursing sessions.

95

Bottle-nosed dolphin, 150–200 kg

Of the three cetacean suborders, only two are extant today. The Odontoceti, or toothed whales, are relatively small and include the dolphins and porpoises. They have conical teeth with which they capture, but do not chew, fish, octopi, nautili, and squid. A single blowhole, actually a nostril, is located at the top of the head and closes when a toothed whale submerges. Upon surfacing, the whale exhales and expels water vapor, which condenses in the air.

The Mysticeti, or baleen whales, are less numerous than the Odontoceti. They eat plankton, which they filter through large plates in their jaws. Also known as whalebone whales, the baleens have a double blowhole and no true teeth.

Whaling has been practiced since 2200 B.C., and meat and oil have been among the rewards. Today there are many substitutes for whale-derived products, yet whales are still extensively hunted for use in such things as pet foods and cosmetics. As a result, their continued existence is seriously threatened.

Bottle-nosed Dolphin

Tursiops truncatus

Bottle-nosed dolphins find food and orient themselves primarily by echolocation. They emit high-pitched clicks that bounce off objects in their path, then back to the dolphins, to be picked up by bones in the lower jaw. These dolphins communicate among themselves via a complex language of whistles. They are very solicitous of one another's welfare, and distress signals sounded by an ailing dolphin usually muster the healthy dolphins' support. It is believed that bottle-nosed dolphins can click and whistle simultaneously, which suggests that their echolocation and communication systems are separately housed, or that the body parts involved in sound production are multifunctional.

Bottle-nosed dolphins are popular aquarium performers. They astonish trainers with their low tolerance for boredom, and may complicate the rules when games become dull.

These dolphins swim in shallow seas around the world, in groups of up to several hundred. They often move with the fish they eat, and may be seen leaping gracefully through the water as they follow boats and ships.

Killer whale, 800–900 kg

Killer Whale

Orcinus orca

The killer whale is actually the largest dolphin, measuring about 6 meters in length and weighing about 900 kilograms. By now it has been observed often, having been captured frequently and trained to appear in marine-life shows. In captivity it generally becomes quite docile, belying its name by allowing trainers to ride it and even to place their heads in its open jaws. In oceans throughout the world, however, killer whales travel rapidly in packs and attack everything from sea lion pups to other whales. They have been seen tossing turtles and sea lions into the air before eating them, and porpoises and fish are supposedly played with the same way before they are consumed. The killer whale is the only cetacean that eats warm-blooded vertebrates.

The older males are easy to spot because of their very long dorsal fins, held upright during swimming. They have been known to patrol the shoreline while the females and juveniles hunt for prey in shallow waters. These distinctively marked whales are not thought to migrate.

Pilot Whale, or Blackfish

Globicephala sp.

The gregarious pilot whale, or blackfish, is known to migrate. Like its look-alike the false killer whale, it seems remarkably willing to follow a leader anywhere, and entire herds end up stranded on shore or taken by whalers in Newfoundland, Japan, and other parts of its nearly worldwide range (it does not frequent polar waters). One widely accepted theory is that the whales beach themselves because ear parasites have interfered with their ability to echolocate. In the North Atlantic the pilot whale migration parallels that of one type of squid, a mainstay of this toothed whale's diet.

It is fortunate for the procreation of the species that pilot whales are polygamous, since females reach sexual maturity at age six, males not till age thirteen. After a gestation period of about a year, a single calf is born. At birth it measures approximately one-third the adult length; adults measure between 3.6 and 8.5 meters.

Like the adults, young pilot whales sometimes beach themselves. Perhaps they get lost. Whatever the causes, they are suspected to be very different from the causes associated with the stranded herds mentioned above.

Minke Whale

Balaenoptera acutorostrata

The minke, or piked, whale is the smallest of five species of whales known as rorquals, a subclassification of the baleens. Rorquals are slender whales with parallel skin grooves running lengthwise from the chin to the chest. The humpback whale, whose lengthy "songs" have been recorded, is a rorqual, as is the blue whale, the largest of all cetaceans. Rorquals form the primary catch for modern whaling, more minkes being taken throughout their worldwide range than any other baleen.

Baleen whales feed in one of three ways. Some "skim," or swim near the surface of the water with the mouth open. Gray whales feed mainly on bottom-dwelling invertebrates. And rorquals "gulp" their food—they take in large quantities of plankton by the mouthful, occasionally getting a sea bird as well.

Considered highly migratory, minke whales invade pack ice more than the other rorquals. The males swim much deeper than the females and young. Schools regularly number up to twenty individuals, sometimes many more.

99

▲ Minke whale, 22.7 metric tons
◀ Pilot whale, 670–690 kilograms

Carnivora

Carnivores are adapted to hunt and kill for food. They have clawed feet and well-developed canines, and most have modified cheek teeth called carnassials, used for shearing flesh. They also have highly specialized sensory organs, for locating prey. The sense of smell is particularly well developed in members of the canine family, for example, whereas vision is specialized in the cats. In contrast to their highly specialized senses, the skeletons of carnivores are very generalized. That is, since these predators have to run, to pounce in order to kill, perhaps to drag their prey or even to climb or swim with it, their skeletons are constructed in such a way as to accommodate a variety of movements.

One meal of protein-rich meat supplies carnivores with nutrients for several hours. Because of this they do not need to spend a great deal of time eating, as many herbivores do. The long periods between hunts afford opportunities for play and other activities that strengthen social bonds and organization, and so indirectly contribute to the strong family units that characterize many members of this order.

Sea lions, seals, and walruses were once classified as a suborder of the carnivores, but are now assigned their own order, Pinnipedia. There are now seven families of carnivores generally recognized—the Canidae (doglike mammals), Viverridae (mongooses and related mammals), Felidae (cats), Mustelidae (muskproducers), Hyaenidae (hyaenas), Ursidae (bears), and Procyonidae (raccoons, pandas, and relatives). Members of the last two families have the most varied diets. Particularly as they emerge from hibernation, they often eat far more herbaceous matter than they do meat. **101**

Cougar, 35–100 kg

It is ironic that carnivores are much maligned for their predation, for they actually serve to keep prey populations healthy by culling the weak and the sick. Carnivores are ultimately dependent on their prey for survival, and in fact experience population fluctuations parallel to their prey's in many cases.

Cougar
Felis concolor

The cougar, now found only in wilderness areas of the North American West, was once distributed over a wider range than any other mammal in the Americas. When the felling of forests brought about a drastic decline in the number of deer, its chief prey animal, the cougar was forced to turn to domestic stock for much of its food. It has not fared well under these conditions: today the eastern cougar is endangered, and the western cougar seems headed in that direction.

The cougar, also known as the mountain lion or the puma, is a secretive cat. The male becomes very high-strung during the breeding period, which may occur at any time of year. If the female does not protect her litter, the male may eat the two or three kittens he has sired. As far as is known, the cougar is one of only a few cats that exhibit this behavior. Such cannibalism may serve to keep the number of cougars at an optimal level: it is known that populations tend to be fairly stable. Kittens that survive begin chewing on bones and eating meat at only six to seven weeks, but they are not fully independent until they are almost two years old.

Bengal Tiger
Leo tigris tigris

The ferocity of tigers, especially the man-eaters, has been greatly exaggerated; there is no doubt, however, that these beautiful cats are masters of the hunt. Formerly, Indian, or Bengal, tigers fed on wild pigs and deer, but due to declines in India's wildlife, tigers now prey on domestic cattle and buffalo. These carnivores are fast disappearing from temperate and tropical Asia, and are officially considered endangered.

Bengal tiger, 225–275 kg

Bengal tigers are well camouflaged for their shadowy forest habitat, and stalk their prey in dense cover until they are within 18–28 meters of it. Then they charge, tail up, in several 6-meter bounds. They usually attack the prey's neck, and are thought to strangle it. Tigers usually hide their kill and leave the vicinity until dark, when they return to eat. Manchurian tigers have been known to consume 32 kilograms at a meal, and eat only once every five or six days.

When a female tiger comes into oestrus (her fertile period), she roars to notify nearby males. The males battle furiously until a winner emerges, but he must be accepted by the tigress herself before mating can occur. Before submitting, she displays a series of what can only be called typical feline gestures— playing with the male's whiskers, rolling on her back with her paws in the air, and so forth. The gestation period is fourteen to sixteen weeks, and two or three cubs are usually born. They begin accompanying their mother on hunts before they are eight weeks old, and are hunting on their own at six months.

Lion

Leo leo

Whereas the other big cats are solitary, lions usually live in prides, loosely structured family groups composed of two to four adult males and perhaps twice that many females with their young. The lionesses are obviously companionable with one another (the playful cubs are frequently accompanied on hunts by an ''aunt'' as well as their mother), less so with the heavily maned males. They seldom associate with nomadic lionesses.

Communication among pride members is complex, and includes close-range signals such as head-rubbing, licking, anal sniffing, and varied facial expressions, positions, and vocalizations. The roar is the main long-distance signal—communal roaring may help to strengthen social bonds.

Lions are at the top of the food chain, with no natural enemies but man and in some cases wild dogs. Their varied diet includes crocodiles, guinea fowl, antelopes, baboons, and even other lions, and they are not above taking the remains of another predator's kill. Lions hunt by stalking, which is difficult because of the lack of cover where they live—the open, dry parts of Africa. Pride members may hunt cooperatively, and they frequently share a kill, often one that is brought down by a lioness.

Polar Bear

Thalarctos maritimus

Wherever seals live in the Arctic, the solitary polar bear may be found hunting. Camouflaged by its coat, it stalks the seals carefully, placing its large paws far apart to distribute body weight. Fur on the bottom of the feet serves as insulation against the cold of snow and ice.

Polar bears are wonderful swimmers and divers, and are often found far out at sea, where they can sniff out prey from over a mile away. Except for pregnant females, these bears do not hibernate, but search for food in their year-round wanderings. Some of them eat tundra vegetation after the dark Arctic winter has subsided. They also take an occasional sea bird.

Every other January twin cubs are born, usually in a den formed of drifted snow and piled-up ice. They stay with their mother for about a year and a half, after which time the female usually accepts another mate.

Polar bears are hunted by Eskimos for their fur as well as for their tendons and fat. Walruses probably rate as the polar bear's second greatest enemy, as their tusks can spell certain death. **105**

▲ Polar bear, 300 kg (females), 400 kg (males)
◀ Lions, 180–225 kg

American Black Bear

Euarctos americanus

Of the four bear species found in North America, the black bear is the smallest and the most widely distributed. In its brown color phase it may occasionally be confused with the grizzly, but it can be distinguished from the grizzly by its straight facial and back profiles. It is also much shyer than the grizzly, and will climb a tree rather than confront a human being. (Panhandling in the national parks is an obvious exception to this rule.)

The black bear eats voraciously in the autumn, storing up fat for its winter sleep, which is not a true hibernation. During its sleep a fecal "plug" develops, which stops the alimentary tract from functioning. Upon emerging in the spring, the bear expels this plug, and within a week or two its digestive system is readjusted to processing food. Instead of carnassials, this omnivorous mammal has molars adapted to crushing its food.

The black bear is nomadic over its entire range—the mountainous forests north of central Mexico, as far north as northwestern Alaska. Every other winter the female usually bears two or three cubs, which weigh only 220 grams each. She cares for them until their sixteenth month.

American black bear, 120–150 kg

Spotted Hyaena

Crocuta crocuta

These aggressive mammals are by no means solely scavengers, as was thought for many years. Like most carnivores, though, they will not refuse carrion, and they may try to drive away lions who seem bent on taking over carcasses they have claimed. Hyaenas may whoop and "laugh" loudly as they crowd around a fresh kill, and the sound often attracts other carnivores to the site. They most often attack the calves or the infirm of wildebeest (one adult wildebeest provides food for a dozen hyaenas). They also prey upon zebras and gazelles. Hyaenas do not stalk or lie in ambush, but chase their prey, usually in packs, often attaining speeds up to 50 kilometers per hour before pulling it down. Blunt conical teeth and specialized stomachs equip hyaenas to eat even the largest bones of their prey: rarely is the site of a kill left anything but clean.

The clan is the hyaena's basic social unit. Communal dens are located in the center of territories used for defecation. Packs patrol the territorial borders and regulate the numbers of nomadic and other hyaenas allowed into the area. The spotted hyaena lives in Africa south of the Sahara.

107

Spotted hyaenas, 60–85 kg

Mongoose

Herpestes sp.

The sight of a mongoose killing a snake is arresting, to say the least. Today such attacks are commonly staged for tourists in India, where mongooses have been the subject of folk literature for centuries. In the wild, these mammals are said to coat themselves with several layers of mud, for protection during fights with serpents. However, it is probably their agility in avoiding bites that protects the mongooses—they are not totally immune to snake venom, as was once suspected.

Originally found solely in the Old World, these carnivores have been brought to such places as Jamaica and Trinidad to be rat-catchers. However, they soon become pests themselves if not carefully controlled. They hunt singly or in small groups, and they eat many kinds of small invertebrates in addition to their more spectacular prey. Some species crack open snails, eggs, and other hard foods by throwing them backward, between their hind legs, onto solid objects. This type of behavior is often carried over into their play sessions, which may include sexual play and mock fighting.

Thought to be territorial, mongooses often do handstands in order to mark trees and other signposts with scent from their anal glands. Their enemies are domestic dogs and people; the latter eat them in many parts of their range.

Most mongooses inhabit Africa; the dozen or so *Herpestes* **108** species also range into Spain, Portugal, and Southeast Asia.

Mongoose, 500 grams–3.2 kg

Sea Otter

Enhydra lutris

Found near the Aleutians and several other islands in the Bering Sea and the northern Pacific, as well as off the coast of California, this cousin of the smaller river otter is considered wholly aquatic. The single offspring stays with its mother for about fifteen months, perching on her chest as she floats on her back, and nestling in the crook of her arm when she dives for food. When she eats, the mother places her offspring in a bed of seaweed, where it is held securely until she can pick it up again. Adult sea otters also wrap themselves in seaweed to keep from drifting away at night and during storms.

The sea otter breaks open the shells of the the marine animals on which it feeds by holding them on its chest and smashing them with a rock. The rock, which is also used to pry shellfish from the ocean floor, may get tucked under a skin fold when the otter swims. In a display of ''handedness'' that is extremely rare in animals other than human beings, the sea otter seems consistently to favor its right forepaw over its left.

Unlike most aquatic mammals, the sea otter has no layer of blubber under its skin. Instead it is covered with long dense fur that traps air and insulates its body. A mother will groom her newborn for hours to rid its fur of moisture so that air can get under it. Oil spills can spell doom for these mammals.

At one time entire herds of sea otters were wiped out by hunters greedy for their gorgeous fur. Today, however, only the killer whale is an immediate threat.

Sea otter, 15–30 kg (females), 25–35 kg (males)

Timber Wolf

Canis lupus

Wolves, jackals, dingoes, foxes, and coyotes all belong to the dog family, the Canidae. Along with the cats and hyaenas, they walk digitigrade, and thereby "increase" the length of their legs.

The wolf's lanky build helps it chase and bring down prey, which ranges from deer and moose to smaller animals such as rodents. Contrary to popular notion, timber wolves do not usually hunt out of greed; like other animals, they simply provide enough food for their young and themselves whenever they can. Wolves are faithful parents, and they live in close-knit, rigidly hierarchical packs. They often stay with the same mate for life.

Wolves can be distinguished from coyotes by their larger body size and by the higher, straighter carriage of their tails. Whereas coyotes do not seem threatened, four species of wolves are on the endangered list, the eastern timber wolf of North America among them. Historically that species has ranged over most of North America, but because of pressures from man, it is now restricted to the north-central United States and the wilderness areas of Canada and Alaska.

Eastern Gray Fox

Urocyon cinereoargenteus

Shyer and smaller than the crafty red fox, the gray fox is the only American canine that climbs trees. Sometimes it climbs just for a casual view, other times to escape a bobcat, a coyote, or some other predator. Thick woodland, swampland, or chaparral is its habitat in Mexico, Central America, and the eastern and southwestern United States. It ranges up the western coast of the United States as far as the state of Washington, and is often seen in the western national parks.

Gray foxes mate in February or March, and about seven weeks later a litter of three to seven is born, usually in natural cavities rather than in excavated dens. As is typical of many canines, both parents care for their offspring, and eventually teach them to hunt mice, rabbits, and other small mammals. Although they may take an occasional chicken, gray foxes are actually a help to farmers, since they eat large numbers of rodents that would probably otherwise ravage crops.

111

▲ Eastern gray fox, 2.5–7 kg
◀ Timber wolf, 25–75 kg

Raccoon

Procyon lotor

The raccoon's habit of washing its food has been the subject of much speculation. It may stem from a concern for cleanliness, or perhaps the dunking itself gives pleasure, since the raccoon has sensitive hands. If it is near water, a raccoon will eat snails, crayfish, mussels, and other aquatic food; if not, it eats melons, corn, berries, and eggs.

These familiar masked, nocturnal mammals have long been hunted for their meat and fur, and their striped tails have been used as ornaments on everything from automobile dashboards to hats. Although hunting dogs often tree them, ''coons'' will not hesitate to fight an entire pack. They are active year-round except in the really cold parts of their range (southern Canada into Central America). In the North they sleep through the winter, but do not truly hibernate.

Raccoons spend their daylight hours in hollow trees or abandoned burrows, where in the spring they produce three to six young. They are independent by the time they are a year old.

Raccoon, 1.5–20 kg

Giant Panda

Ailuropoda melanoleuca

One of the favorites at the zoo, the giant panda invites sentimentalizing—its large "black eyes" and rolling gait are endearing.

The giant panda can pull individual bamboo leaves from their stems without so much as bruising them; it owes this manual dexterity to specialized pads on its forepaws. Bamboo leaves and shoots form the primary, and sometimes the sole, diet of the giant panda, which eats from ten to twelve hours a day in the wilds of central and western China. In spite of its penchant for vegetable matter, this mammal is considered a carnivore, as it will take meat on occasion.

The giant panda does not reach sexual maturity until its fourth year. This is not as advanced an age as it sounds, for the young, born after a gestation period of about nine months, weigh only about 2 kilograms each at birth. In the wild, the giant panda's average life span is fourteen to eighteen years. The adults are solitary animals, active throughout the year.

Classification of the giant and lesser pandas has presented scientists with certain problems. Giant pandas look like bears, lesser pandas like raccoons. The dilemma was solved by a decision to classify pandas with the raccoon, not on the basis of external appearance, but on the basis of similarities between the two animals' reproductive organs and scent glands.

Giant panda, 75–150 kg

Stoat

Mustela erminea

Weasels are dauntless fighters. Their serpentine bodies allow them to enter the burrows of prey animas such as rabbits and rodents. They kill by inflicting a bite, with lightninglike speed, at the base of the prey animal's skull. They then consume the meat, bones, and skin of their prey.

The stoat (known as the ermine in the New World) is a fur-bearer found worldwide. Its famous white coat with black tips is its winter pelage only; in warm weather the stoat's fur turns brown. Female stoats undergo a phenomenon known as delayed implantation: after fertilization, a period of time elapses before the egg is implanted in the uterus. This adaptation is a form of population control common to several mammal species.

The mink, a New World mustelid similar in habit to the stoat, ranges over most of North America. Its diet includes a large proportion of fish, as well as muskrat; its habitat is along stream and lake banks. A mink's musk attracts members of the opposite sex, yet its stench is, at least to human nostrils, even more acrid than the skunk's. Wild mink have had their numbers reduced by extensive trapping for pelts. Today, however, most skins used in mink coats and other garments come from fur "ranches."

Striped Skunk

Mephitis mephitis

Two species of striped skunks, the African polecats and weasels, two species of spotted skunks, and the hog-nosed skunks all have two things in common—they defend themselves with an extraordinarily pungent scent, supposedly powerful enough to choke some victims by inhibiting breathing; and they are marked with conspicuous black-and-white patterns that act as a warning to other species. These musk-producers rarely conceal themselves, since they have little to fear.

The striped skunk inhabits North America from southern Canada as far south as Central America. It raises its long, bushy tail before it expels musk from scent glands located near the anus. Some foot-stomping, hair-raising, and back-arching may accompany the discharge. The musk can cause human eyes to burn intensely, but it does no permanent harm.

Caterpillars, birds' eggs, bees, corn, grasshoppers, fruits, and meadow mice make up the striped skunk's diet. In northern climates this mammal becomes inactive for most of the winter, in southern climates for only a few days.

After a gestation period of a little more than two months, the striped skunk bears four to six young. By the time the animals are two months old their scent glands are fully developed.

115

▲ Striped skunk, 1–2.5 kg
◀ Stoat, 40–250 grams

Pinnipedia

True seals, fur seals and sea lions, and walruses make up the order Pinnipedia, which means "fin-footed." True seals have streamlined bodies, with no external ears or reproductive organs. Their furred hind flippers point backward and propel them through the water, but make for slow, awkward movement on land. Fur seals and sea lions have small external ears and sexual organs; on land they use all four flippers to "walk" and even to gallop. The front flippers provide swimming and steering power.

Pinnipeds are not wholly aquatic. Many species go ashore periodically, and large congregations of them return to the same place each year to bear and suckle their young.

California Sea Lion

Zalophus californianus

Zalophus californianus is the clever circus "seal." Gregarious year-round, this mammal is known for its playfulness in the wild—it barks and honks at the slightest provocation. The tricks it is trained to perform show off its natural coordination.

The sea lion is found in temperate to subtropical waters along the coastal areas of California, the Galapagos Islands, and the Southern Sea of Japan. Its coat, black when wet, dries to a buff or brown on land. Like all eared seals, the California sea lion "walks" on land fairly easily. It feeds on squid, octopi, and fish.

The bull's shaggy neck and shoulder mane gives this pinniped its leonine name. Bulls assemble harems during the breeding season. After mating and a gestation period of some 350 days, the single pups are born. **117**

California sea lion, 80–90 kg (females), 250–280 kg (males)

Walrus

Odobenus rosmarus

The walrus has tusks and bristly whiskers. The latter are excellent sensory organs; the former are used for digging up the ocean floor in search of bivalves. (Fleshy clams may be extracted from their shells by sucking; whether the shells are actually taken into the mouth and crushed by the teeth is not known.) The tusks also dig into ice and provide leverage as the heavy walrus pulls itself onto a floe; and they are used by bulls to strike out at rivals. (The thick skins of older males may be covered with scars, evidence of a lifetime of skirmishes.) Walruses do not assemble harems. They are highly thigmotactic—that is, they stay in close physical contact with each other, and thus share body heat.

The pharynx of this pinniped is elastic and can be inflated at will. It serves to aid flotation during a nap or a swim; it also provides a resonating chamber for the bell-like sounds the walrus produces. These noises alert walrus hunters to their prey's whereabouts. Oil, tusks, skins, and other parts of the walrus's body have long supplied Arctic peoples with their basic needs. Recent declines in walrus populations, however, have necessitated restricted hunting practices throughout the walrus's range, which is that part of the Arctic Ocean near polar ice.

Elephant Seal

Mirounga sp.

Like their namesakes the elephants, these seals are the largest members of their order: bulls reach weights up to 3.5 metric tons. During mating season, when the bulls become sexually aroused, their proboscis becomes inflated to twice its usual size. Though it seems to have no effect in attracting females to the harem, the enlarged trunk does contribute to the fierce appearance of individuals doing battle, and it may function as a resonator for the bull's trumpeting calls.

These seals congregate ashore and fast during the breeding and molting seasons. (At other times they feed on fish and cuttlefish, for which they may dive several hundred meters.) Females deliver their single pups soon after the rookeries are established in the spring, and mate again within two to three weeks. Gestation lasts about 350 days.

Both species of elephant seal have recovered from earlier sealing practices which drastically reduced their numbers. The northern species, *Mirounga angustirostris*, inhabits the west coast of North America as far north as central California. The more populous species, *M. leonina*, breeds off the coast of Argentina and south to the Antarctic Circle. **119**

▲ Elephant seal, 900 kg–3.5 metric tons
◄ Walrus, 650–850 kg (females), 1–1.25 metric tons (males)

Harbor Seal

Phoca vitulina

In some cases, the natal coat of the infant harbor seal is shed before birth. Generally, though, it isn't until the newborn is two or three weeks old that the white, woolly natal coat is replaced by a silver, brown, black, or grayish one, which may be ringed or spotted. These and other earless seals are born on land, and suckle for only a brief time before they take to the ocean: their greater maneuverability in water makes them less vulnerable to predators there than on land.

The harbor seal propels itself with a side-to-side motion of the hind flippers. It navigates by using echolocation along with its sharp vision, the latter made possible by a flat cornea capable of focusing underwater. Scientists have yet to discover why this seal swallows stones, or why it seems to weep perpetually. It may be that the harbor seal's eyes tear constantly because it cannot utilize the ocean water it drinks until the salt has been excreted through the tear ducts.

The harbor seal is found in the coastal waters of the northern hemisphere. It also follows prey fish into fresh-water rivers. The killer whale is its primary marine enemy.

▲ Harbor seal, 80–90 kg (females), 100 kg (males)
Northern fur seals, 35–70 kg (females), 185–300 kg (males) ▶

Northern Fur Seal

Callorhinus ursinus

Summer brings the northern fur seals to their breeding grounds in the Bering Sea. The bulls reach the Pribilof Islands early, from their wintering grounds off Alaska's southern coast, and they battle each other fiercely for the territories in which they will keep their harems. In June the cows arrive from far to the south. They are significantly smaller than the bulls, and lack the thickened neck that marks the males. Pregnant when they arrive, they soon bear and begin to suckle their single pups, and several days thereafter they mate. Because of the phenomenon known as delayed implantation, the newly conceived pups are not born until the following summer. Northern fur seal mothers alternate periods of nursing with their own sometimes extensive feeding trips in the sea (fish, squid, and crustaceans make up the diet). In November the seals begin to migrate southward, the males to Alaska's waters, the females much farther south. Many of them do not stop until they reach the waters off Mexico's coast.

Sharks prey on these seals, but are not capable of wholesale slaughter such as that inflicted by man in the eighteenth and nineteenth centuries. Clubbed almost to extinction for their luxurious coats, the species was finally saved by a 1911 agreement signed by Canada, Japan, Russia, and the United States limiting the number that could be killed annually. Today about 1.5 million individuals return to the Pribilofs each year.

Tubulidentata

The order Tubulidentata has only one member —the aardvark. Its name, which means "earth-pig" in Afrikaans, well befits this swinelike mammal, with its unsurpassed digging ability.

Aardvarks have a very specialized dentition —the teeth in the front of the mouth develop first, then fall out as the animal matures. An adult has only rear teeth, which work with its long tongue to capture and consume insects.

Aardvark

Orycteropus afer

The aardvark is a termite-eater in areas where those insects may reach 2.5 centimeters in length. Like the pangolins and anteaters, this mammal has a sticky tongue with which it captures its prey. It supposedly hears or smells termites on the march, and simply extends its tongue up to 30 centimeters to reach them. Its clawed feet rip open hard insect mounds, and although soldier termites swarm over the aardvark, they cannot penetrate its thick skin.

This mammal is an extraordinary burrower. It inhabits open areas in Africa south of the Sahara, where the ground is often baked hard by the sun. This is no deterrent to the aardvark, whose strong front feet dig right through the solid earth. It can excavate burrows up to 3 meters long, with a chamber at the end large enough for the animal to turn around in. The aardvark sleeps during the day and usually forages only by night.

This strong mammal prefers to elude enemies rather than fight them. But it can use its tail and claws against lions and other predators if it must.

Aardvark, 50–80 kg

Proboscidea

During the Pleistocene epoch numerous trunked animals, or proboscideans, roamed the earth. Today the African elephant and the smaller Asiatic, or Indian, elephant represent the entire Proboscidean order. The former is the largest land mammal living today: it reaches a weight of 7.5 metric tons.

African Elephant

Loxodonta africana

Marvelously intelligent and gregarious, African elephants communicate with each other by means of numerous sounds produced by their trunks, their mouths, and their stomachs. The large ears, when spread, can catch the slightest of these noises, and even a small flick of the ear itself can signal acceptance or rejection. Trunks are capable of determining scent direction and wind force, and the fingerlike projections near the tip are refined foraging tools. Like the ear, the trunk itself is expressive, as it slaps, caresses, and explores during mating and the discipline of the young.

Most African elephants live in herds of ten to twenty, and require enormous amounts of water for drinking and bathing. A single individual may eat 150 kilograms of vegetable matter in a day. It is no wonder, then, that the herds cause severe damage to trees and other plants when they are overcrowded in their savannah or forest habitat.

Healthy adult African elephants have no natural enemies. However, they have been hunted for ivory so extensively that they are now entirely absent from the northern regions of their continent.

African elephant, 5–7.5 metric tons

Hyracoidea

Members of the order Hyracoidea are known as both hyraxes and dassies. They all belong to a single family, which is divided into three genera. One of these contains the arboreal hyraxes, the other two the terrestrial species. Members of all three genera have small hoofs on their toes, which help make them expert climbers.

Hyraxes resemble the rodents and lagomorphs in both size and habit, the terrestrial species behaving very much like the pikas.

Rock Hyrax

Heterohyrax sp.

Native African legend holds that hyraxes are the only animals that can look straight at the sun. In fact, their eyes do possess a specialized iris which seems to keep out damaging rays, and sunshine apparently agrees with them. Probably because they are well insulated by their thick fur, they are able to bask on incredibly hot rocks without showing the slightest sign of becoming overheated.

Rock hyraxes are playful and keen-witted. In the mornings and evenings they feed in groups on roots, bulbs, and locusts. If they are threatened by a rock python or bird of prey, they dash to shelter among the rocks, squealing loudly in alarm. The soles of their feet are kept moist by secretions from specialized glands, and their foot muscles actually contract to form an air-tight "suction cup" that grips smooth surfaces. This adaptation enables hyraxes to cling to near-vertical rock faces.

The six species of rock hyraxes range from Ethiopia through the Congo and south to southern South-West Africa.

127

Rock hyrax, 475 grams – 4.5 kg

Sirenia

Dugongs and manatees compose the order known as Sirenians, named for the legendary Greek sirens, who used seductive songs to destroy mariners. They are the only wholly herbivorous marine mammals.

Sirenians inhabit shallow coastal areas—manatees are found in the western hemisphere, dugongs in the eastern. Both have almost hairless skin which (like cetaceans' skin) helps streamline the animals for their marine life style. Most adults range in length between 2.5 and 4 meters.

Florida Manatee

Trichechus manatus

The Florida manatee has very long lungs (about 90 centimeters) and can remain underwater for fifteen-minute feeding sessions. Its flippers, which may be used for "walking" in very shallow waters, also direct vegetation to the manatee's cleft upper lip, where bristles help work food into the mouth.

This manatee lives off Florida's western coast, in the Caribbean, and off the eastern shore of South America. It also ranges into coastal rivers.

Prior to mating, the male nuzzles and caresses the female. Gestation lasts about 170 days, and the single calf is born underwater, just as cetacean young are. It may ride its mother piggyback, and it nurses for a year and a half.

Because they are sluggish mammals, manatees are fairly easily caught, and they have been hunted for generations for their fine meat. Excessive hunting, and a number of accidents in which manatees have been killed as a result of getting caught in motorboat propellers, have led to their endangered status.

Florida manatee, 150–350 kg

Perissodactyla

Members of the order Perissodactyla are ungulates (hoofed animals) with an odd number of toes on each foot. The body weight of perissodactyls rests on the central digit alone (which is the only digit in the case of horses), whereas in the artiodactyls (even-toed ungulates) the body weight rests on more than one digit.

Perissodactyls move on their hooves, actually their toenails. All three families are exclusively herbivorous, either as browsers or grazers.

Grant's Zebra

Equus burchelli

Zebras are clearly members of the genus *Equus*, as are burros, asses, domestic horses, and the sole surviving species of wild horse. The three zebra species are distinguished not only by their stripes, but also by size, ear shape, and the patterning on the legs. Except for mountain zebras, they inhabit the plains and savannahs of east, central, and southern Africa.

Zebras defend themselves from lions and hyaenas by biting and kicking furiously, but they seem to surrender as soon as they sense defeat. It is thought that zebras become insentient and go into shock just before they are brought down. If this is true, it may be a protective adaptation common to many species that are consumed while still alive.

Grant's zebras form family groups of a stallion, five or six mares, and their young. Stallions without mates usually form bachelor groups, though some are solitary. First foals are born when the mares are three years old, after a gestation period of a little over a year.

Grant's zebra, 350 kg

African Black Rhinoceros

Diceros bicornis

Huge platelike folds of skin and a single horn distinguish the three Asian rhinoceros species. The two African species have two horns and no skin folds. Of the five species, only the African black rhino, found in eastern and southern Africa, still exists in significant numbers. However, its horns, prized for their supposed aphrodisiac powers and therefore avidly sought after by hunters, may yet be its downfall.

One of the largest land mammals, the black rhino may reach a weight of 1.8 metric tons. Only elephants and the African white rhino (also called the square-lipped rhino) are bigger. Rather ill-tempered, the black rhino puffs and snorts when angered, especially when it charges. Vehicles are charged regularly, and men have been thrown into the air by this rhino's front horn.

The black rhino browses in the mornings and evenings, and retires to the shade of trees during the afternoon. It defecates only in certain areas of its dry, scrubby habitat, probably to mark territories, and it wallows often in mud holes and sandy riverbeds. The black rhino inhabits eastern and southern Africa.

Black rhinos can breed at any time of year. The gestation period is up to eighteen months, and a single young is born.

African black rhinoceros, 1–1.8 metric tons

Baird's Tapir

Tapirus bairdi

Only four species of tapirs exist today. One of them, the Malayan tapir, inhabits eastern India and Malaya; the other three have separate ranges in Central and South America. Fossil records show, however, that many additional species have lived at various times in America and Asia.

The tapir is considered rather primitive because it has a low, plump shape and its teeth are unspecialized. However, it has a very sensitive nose at the end of its trunk, and its upper lip (also part of the trunk) is extremely efficient in gathering the leaves, grasses, and fruits on which the tapir feeds. The trunk itself can be extended and contracted and is covered with bristles that are actually tactile organs.

The tapir, solitary and shy, usually stays on or near a path that leads to water. When disturbed by a jaguar or some other enemy, it leaves its path and crashes wildly through its dense jungle habitat. It frequently wallows in the mud to help control the insects that bother it, and it often has a layer of dried mud on its skin. Newborns' coats have pronounced yellowish bands and spots, which gradually fade in six to eight months.

Tapirs are fast disappearing, due to habitat destruction and other pressures. The Central American tapir, which is almost extinct in Mexico, is considered an endangered species.

133

Baird's tapir, 230–290 kg

Artiodactyla

Like perissodactyls, artiodactyls are ungulates. Members of the two orders differ primarily in the number of toes they have—most artiodactyls have an even number. Their weight rests on the two central digits rather than on a single digit. ("Cloven-hoofed" describes artiodactyls with two digits only.) This type of foot structure, along with an anklebone that allows much freedom of movement, helps account for the swiftness that characterizes so many artiodactyls.

Nine families make up this order. They are classified mainly on the basis of the structure and function of digestive systems. A two- or three-chambered nonruminating stomach characterizes the pigs (families Suidae and Tayassuidae) and hippopotamuses (Hippopotamidae). A three-chambered ruminating stomach characterizes the camels (Camelidae) and the mouse deer and chevrotains (Tragulidae). The remaining species, the vast majority of artiodactyls, are the true ruminants; most have four-chambered stomachs. These are the deer (Cervidae), the giraffes (Giraffidae), and the antelopes, sheep, and cattle (Antilocapridae and Bovidae).

The vegetation on which ruminants browse or graze is relatively low in food value, so these animals must eat large quantities of food to obtain sufficient nutrients. Grazing therefore occupies a great deal of a ruminant's time, often in open terrain where predation is easy. It would occupy even more time were it not for rumination. By this process animals swallow their food whole or nearly whole, and it goes into the first of four stomach chambers. There it is acted upon by bacteria that begin to break down the cellulose in the grasses and woody fibers, helping to free the nutrients therein. After passing **135**

Bison, 450 kg–1.3 metric tons

through a second chamber, the food is regurgitated into the mouth. In this stage the food is known as "cud," and the animal is said to "chew the cud." When it has blended with saliva, the food is swallowed a second time, and goes into a third chamber. From there it enters the fourth chamber, where the final and most thorough digestive activity takes place.

The fossil record of the artiodactyls and perissodactyls is rather complete, partly because large bones are preserved by nature more easily than smaller bones, and the members of both orders have massive bones indeed. It is clear that most of the present-day artiodactyls evolved from original Old World stock, the perissodactyls from New World stock. The first artiodactyls had four digits on each foot, and a very generalized dentition. As members of the order evolved, there was a tendency for the number of digits to become reduced, and for tooth structure to become specialized along with the evolution of the ruminating stomach. From these beginnings developed the numerous and wonderfully diverse modern artiodactyls.

Bison

Bison bison

For centuries several North American Indian tribes based their entire cultures upon the bison, also called the buffalo. By 1889, however, excessive hunting had reduced a herd of millions to a mere 500 or so individuals. Gradually bison have been brought back from the edge of extinction; today they are found in considerable numbers on government ranges and in private herds.

Bison feed on gray sage, buffalo grass, and other grassland vegetation. North America's largest land mammals, they may reach a weight of 1,350 kilograms. They are gregarious, living in herds that include several generations and are led by an old cow. Bulls tend to become less sociable as they mature, and may break from the herds and form small bands of their own. When opposed by a rival, a bull will wallow in the dust, a habit that also helps rid its large body and shaggy coat of parasites.

The European wisent, primarily a woodland animal, is the only other member of the genus *Bison*. It has a history of exploitation very similar to that of the North American species.

African buffalo, 750 kg

African Buffalo

Syncerus caffer

Buffalo are Africa's only oxlike animals. Horns, overall size, and habitat distinguish two basic types within this species. The smaller of the two, the forest buffalo, is found in western and central Africa; the more massive plains buffalo, commonly known as the cape buffalo, is found in the southern part of the continent. Cape buffalo have a reputation for viciously attacking hunters, but in fact they are often injured or provoked into such behavior. Normally these ruminants are quite placid.

Cape buffalo are truly gregarious. They assemble in herds of up to two thousand head, often accompanied by tickbirds, which prey on the buffalo's skin parasites. Cape buffalo scouts warn of lions and other dangers during grazing, which occupies most of this mammal's evening hours. Like domestic cattle, they require water daily, and they wallow whenever possible; crocodiles occasionally attack them as they are crossing rivers.

Cape buffalo are suspected carriers of the dreaded cattle plague that wiped out thousands of African ungulates in the late nineteenth century. In some places *Syncerus caffer* has still not recovered its former numbers.

Single calves are born to the females after a gestation period of 330 days. They are mature at about two years.

Bighorn Sheep

Ovis canadensis

Wild sheep of the genus *Ovis* fall into five categories—the mouflons of the Mediterranean and Middle Eastern countries, the ammons of central Asia, the Asiatic bighorns of Siberia, the Dall sheep of Alaska and nearby areas, and the North American bighorns of the Rocky Mountains.

Bighorns traverse their craggy terrain on specialized hooves. The hard outer edges protect them from sharp rocks, while the soft underparts aid the sheep in balancing. Females usually choose the least accessible ledges to bear their young.

The dominant characteristic of these bovids is, of course, their horns. They grow continually from the base over a permanent bony core—they are not shed annually. A bighorn's age may be read by the number of corrugations or rings in its horns. The rams bear the massive curled horns, the size of which determines rank—only rams of equal horn size compete for harems. Older rams' horns are often worn, or "broomed" at the tips, from battles that break out during the autumn rut. Because the horns are prized as trophies, these rams have been hunted to the point where the species is now seriously threatened.

Chamois

Rupicapra rupicapra

The chamois can climb practically anywhere. Its hooves, with elastic underparts and hard outer parts, grip slick surfaces and narrow ledges in the mountains of Europe and Asia Minor. This Old World counterpart of the American mountain goat slides down hillsides on its stomach and performs elaborate, graceful "dances," presumably out of sheer joy and energy.

A chamois' age can be read in the rings that encircle its horns—one ring per year. Old chamois males are solitary except during the autumn rut. One or two young are born about 175 days after mating, and can leap about within three or four days. Were this not the case, eagles and other predators would probably take a great toll on the young. Adults are known to stamp their feet and whistle to warn of danger.

In summer the chamois eats mountain herbs and flowers, in winter, lichens and mosses that grow in the valleys. In deep snow it can fast for several days.

▲ Chamois, 25–50 kg
◀ Bighorn sheep, 35–70 kg (females), 55–125 kg (males)

Gerenuk

Litocranius walleri

Antelopes are Old World ruminants that belong to the family Bovidae. They differ from oxen, also Bovidae, in their slighter build, their horns which point upward and backward, and the wide variability in body size. The gerenuk commonly weighs about 45 kilograms and thus is closer in body size to the dik-dik, which is not much larger than a rabbit, than it is to the eland, which can weigh 900 kilograms. All three are antelopes.

In the Somali language the word *gerenuk* means "giraffe-necked." Like a giraffe, this graceful African antelope extends its long neck for browsing on acacias and other foliage; unlike a giraffe, it stands on its hind legs, often with the forelegs propped against a tree trunk. Browsing high in this position, it creates a slender, almost vertical silhouette that is easy to spot.

The gerenuk is one of the few African animals whose range seems to be expanding. Historically it has inhabited the desert areas of eastern Africa.

Common Eland

Taurotragus oryx

The eland, with its prominent dewlap, is Africa's largest antelope. Males may reach weights of over 900 kilograms and shoulder heights of 1.8 meters. Yet both they and the smaller females can leap up to 2.4 meters in the air, sailing over each other's bodies with apparent ease. Both sexes have spiral horns, which they sometimes use to break twigs from branches so they can browse on the leaves. Elands also eat some fruit, and they use their hooves to unearth roots and bulbs. Since they obtain moisture from their food, they do not require water regularly.

These bovids are gregarious, their herds numbering up to two hundred individuals. They stay on the move much of the time, yet because of their unaggressive temperament they are easily approached and captured. (Both their meat and their milk are of high quality, and their hides are often made into leather.)

Common elands range through the grasslands and even into the forests of central and southern Africa. The other eland species, the giant eland, is found in the central and western parts of the continent.

141

▲ Common eland, 600–900 kg
◀ Gerenuks, 40–50 kg

Dik-dik

Madoqua sp.

The dainty, fragile-looking antelopes known as dik-diks are very secretive. About six species inhabit the drier areas of most of Africa, where they remain out of sight in the dense undergrowth. If flushed, they make zigzag leaps to safety, and by doing so often alert larger mammals to danger. Small parties of dik-diks browse by night along well-defined paths; they prefer to eat acacias and fruits.

Pairs of these dwarf ungulates (they weigh only 3–5 kilograms) have been known to occupy the same territory for many years. Fecal marking of territories is common, and both partners contribute to the large piles. The single young stays within its parents' territory for about a year. Then it is driven out by the male, and may lead a solitary existence before it eventually claims a territory of its own.

Dik-diks get their name from their birdlike call of alarm (some listeners think it sounds more like *zik-zik*). They are prey to hunters who sell their skins for gloves, rugs, and other luxury products. Many native peoples are superstitious about killing and eating dik-diks, but others capture and sell them in large numbers.

Dik-dik, 3–5 kg

Grant's Gazelle

Gazella granti

The bewildering array of antelopes and related ungulates includes some dozen or so species of true gazelles, all of them fleet and lyrical creatures with distinctive horns. The Grant's gazelle of eastern Africa is one of the larger. It is often confused with the Thomson's gazelle, though the two differ markedly in rump and facial patterning. It is also sometimes confused with the impala, an antelope known for its incredible leaps.

Gazelles inhabit open, dry terrain, and the Grant's even ranges into semidesert. Because it grazes at night, when its food has absorbed the most moisture, it seldom needs to drink.

Males and their harems roam very large territories which are delineated in several ways—by urination, defecation, and grasses worn down by the long horns. (Females have smaller horns.) "Weaving" is the phrase used to describe the wearing-down process—the male beats the vegetation as he thrusts his head alternately left and right. During courtship a Grant's gazelle buck "marches" the doe forward, then displays a characteristic movement of one foreleg. Copulation takes place as the pair is walking. A single fawn is born, which begins to move about when less than one hour old.

143

Grant's gazelles, 15–75 kg

Klipspringer

Oreotragus oreotragus

"Klipspringer," or "cliffspringer," is an apt name for this antelope. Of all artiodactyls it alone walks on the very tips of its hooves, and it is capable of amazing leaps. The klipspringer lives in rocky, mountainous terrain where footholds are all but invisible, yet it can land (on all four hooves) on a spot no larger than a saucer. Running is actually a series of bouncy hops.

Klipspringers rarely live in groups of more than six. They keep watch from the tops of boulders, and give a sharp nasal whistle when alarmed. They are well camouflaged by their salt-and-pepper coat, which is longer and stiffer than the coats of other African antelopes.

The range of this antelope extends from southern and eastern Africa to the Sudan and Somaliland; it also includes Nigeria. Male klipspringers have been heard to hum softly during mating. After a gestation period of about 214 days, one to three young are born.

Klipspringer, 12–15 kg

Hartebeest

Alcelaphus sp.

Handlebar horns grow on a pedicel (a small stalky support) in both sexes of hartebeests. Horn shape, which varies slightly from species to species, is the most distinctive characteristic of these slant-backed antelopes. Hartebeests belong to the same family as the wildebeests and the topis. All three animals have very distinctive appearances.

Hartebeests are gregarious, and herds of six to twenty may even be found in the company of zebras, waterbucks, and other ungulates. Although they are not normally excitable, years of persecution have taught them to be wary of human beings; they are often preyed upon by lions as well. Hartebeests frequently post "sentries," which, when they sense the approach of a predator or some other threat, communicate a warning to the herd. The herd responds by running single-file at speeds of up to 64 kilometers an hour, snorting through the nose as they go.

Hartebeests inhabit the scrub country just south of the Sahara. **145**

Hartebeest, 165–180 kg

Blue Wildebeest

Connochaetes taurinus

Game cropping, the management of wild species within fenced areas, has saved the black wildebeest from extinction. The practice also provides valuable meat (much needed in Africa) from the animals culled for the long-range health of the herd.

Black wildebeests, also known as white-tailed gnus, perform antics unmatched by any other species. In what can only be called ritualistic clowning, they prance, paw, and kick up their heels in seeming abandon. Blue wildebeests, also called brindled gnus and white-bearded wildebeests, are much calmer. Because they are among the few ungulates with a definite breeding season, they have been the subject of many studies on birth patterns. In the Serengeti ninety-five percent of blue wildebeest females produce a calf annually.

Blue wildebeests have also been closely observed for their herd behavior: large numbers of them often run single-file across the dry plains of southern and southeastern Africa, following food supplies. They feed at any time of day or night, preferably on grass sprouts, and they drink daily when water is available. When it is not, supplements such as wild melons and succulents help them to survive. Blue wildebeest herds withstand heavy predation by lions, cheetahs, wild dogs, and hyaenas. But they suffer huge losses at the hands of poachers

146 who kill them for their tails, which are made into fly whisks.

▲ Blue wildebeests, 250 kg
Pronghorns, 35–60 kg ▶

Pronghorn

Antilocapra americana

The swiftest of New World mammals, pronghorns can run up to 72 kilometers per hour, and have been known to keep pace with cars and other motor vehicles. Though they are not true antelopes, they are the sole surviving members of the family Antilocapridae, which reached its greatest numbers in Miocene and Pliocene times. About 250,000 pronghorns now inhabit the plains of western North America, where they live in winter herds of a hundred head or more. They are the only horned mammals that shed just their horn coverings, not the entire horns, after each breeding season.

Bucks compete for harems in the late summer, and may win as many as fifteen does each. After mating and a gestation period of about 235 days, the female bears one, two, or occasionally three offspring. Helpless for about a week, the young are kept close to the ground several feet apart. If a coyote is nearby, or if some other danger is imminent, an adult will flash its white rump in a warning to its fellows.

Full of curiosity, a pronghorn, when it hears a sudden noise, will usually turn around to see what startled it rather than run. This habit sometimes proves fatal, for it makes the pronghorn an easy victim of predators. Thanks to the work of concerned naturalists, pronghorns now enjoy protection from the wholesale slaughter that earlier caused their numbers to diminish along with millions of American bison.

Red Deer

Cervus elaphus

Red deer are the prototypical deer of Europe. Handsome cousins of the North American wapiti, they are gregarious browsers and grazers in deciduous and some coniferous forests. In Scotland they are adapted to live on the moors.

One of the chief characteristics of red deer is their many-tined antlers, which often have forked tips that form a sort of crown. Antlers, usually present in the males only, are a distinctive feature of the entire deer family (Cervidae); the type of antlers distinguishes genera. In species with a definite breeding season, the antlers begin to grow in early summer. By early fall they are ready to shed their velvet (the thin, finely haired skin that covers them); to aid the process, the buck rubs the antlers against a tree or some other hard object. Shedding velvet is painless, since no blood is left in the antlers by this time. Once exposed, the antlers, with their core of solid bone, are formidable weapons, and thus armed the bucks battle for the harems they will keep through winter mating. By spring the antlers are shed.

Red deer range from Great Britain throughout Europe and Asia, and into northern Africa.

Moose

Alces alces

The moose is the world's largest deer and North America's biggest game animal. Adult bulls may weigh 650 kilograms, and their antlers may measure close to 2 meters across; yet they slip through the dense conifer stands of Canada and the northwestern United States without a sound. And they swim at speeds of up to 56 kilometers per hour.

In summer moose wade on their long legs far out into ponds and lakes to eat water plants, and may kneel on land to reach low-growing sedges and other vegetation. In winter they browse on conifers high above their heads, often while standing on their hind legs.

During the rutting season (September through November) a bull will bugle loudly, often to be answered by a doe's low hoarse calls. Though he does not assemble a harem, he usually mates several times and may fight a rival for a doe. During these fights bulls sometimes lock antlers and are then unable to extricate themselves. Starvation and wolves have both been known to claim the lives of animals immobilized in this way.

▲ Moose, 500–650 kg
◄ Red deer, 125–225 kg

Reindeer

Rangifer tarandus

Reindeer and caribou are both subspecies of *Rangifer tarandus* — caribou are native to the New World and Siberia, reindeer to the Old World and Greenland. In both, male and female bear antlers, a characteristic unique to this species. Antlers may be asymmetrical, and in the adults may overhang the brow, perhaps for protection during combat between rival bucks. The function of the female's antlers is unclear.

Migrations of 600 kilometers or more are common in this species, and are usually triggered by food shortages as the tundra begins to freeze. After the young are born in late summer, herds of up to a thousand individuals often travel into wooded areas (the reindeer's diet includes leaves as well as grasses and lichens). The reindeer's flat, cleft hoof allows for easy movement on soggy land as well as on the snow.

Both caribou and reindeer have been domesticated by Laplanders, Eskimos, and other peoples of the far North, who use **150** the animals for meat and leather.

▲ Reindeer, 250–300 kg
Giraffe, 550 kg–1.8 metric tons ▶

Giraffe

Giraffa camelopardalis

With an adult height of 4.25–5.5 meters, giraffes are the world's tallest animals. They have unique, sometimes knobby, horns, and their skin patterns vary considerably according to region. (Giraffes are found in the drier open parts of Africa south of the Sahara.) Long eyelashes fringe their liquid brown eyes, which have keen vision.

If danger threatens these shy ungulates, the dozen or so herd members may escape by running, for long distances, up to 45 kilometers per hour. When running, the giraffe brings the hind feet in front of the forefeet; the long neck and head are swung in a wide arc, first in one direction, then in the other.

Giraffes thrust their necks into acacia and other branches and grasp the foliage with their long tongues. They can browse up to 6 meters above the ground and can, by spreading their long forelegs far apart, lower their heads enough to reach water at ground level. Though they occasionally lie down to sleep, giraffes usually doze standing.

Males spar year-round, but courting as such is rare. Sometimes a male will collect the female's urine in his mouth, possibly to test hormone content. Giraffes bear single offspring, and are not thought to have strong maternal instincts.

Okapi

Okapia johnstoni

Okapis were unknown outside the Congo's lush forests before about 1900, when their discovery excited scientists worldwide. Pygmies had eaten them and used their hides for centuries, but the animals' elusive habits and dense habitat had kept them a secret from others. Even now, few have been observed in the wild. Okapis are classified with modern-day giraffes, since they are relatives of an extinct form of giraffe that lived some ten million years ago. They have been protected by law since 1933.

This wary chestnut-colored mammal has a tongue so long that it bathes its eyes with it. The tongue also helps in browsing— leaves comprise most of the okapi's diet. Single okapis or very small groups of them wander cautiously on well-worn paths, from which they seem to disappear at the slightest sound.

After much trial and error, okapis became sufficiently acclimated to captivity to be bred. They have a relatively low reproductive rate—a single young is born after a gestation period of about fourteen and a half months. Okapi mothers, unlike giraffe mothers, constantly defend their offspring. They may just threaten, with various head movements, or they may kick violently at intruders.

▲ Okapis, 225 kg
Hippopotamus, 3–4.5 metric tons ▶

Hippopotamus

Hippopotamus amphibius

Grazers by night, hippopotamuses spend most of the daylight hours floating, walking, or just lolling in fresh or brackish waters of south and central Africa. When a hippo dives, its nostrils close; when it surfaces, it whirls its ears independently to clear them of water. Usually hippos submerge for only four or five minutes at a time, but they can remain underwater for up to half an hour if they need to stay out of sight. They have no sweat glands. If they are out of the water for any length of time, they exude a reddish-brown mucus through their pores. This has caused some observers to think hippos "sweat blood." When the mucus dries, it forms a protective coating on the hippo's hide.

Enormous lower canines that grow throughout the hippo's life serve the bulls as weapons against rivals. These teeth were at one time more valued for their ivory than elephant tusks were. On land, bulls scatter their excrement with their tails, probably to mark territories. Excrement deposited in the water nourishes microscopic plants that are eaten by fish.

Female hippos give birth and nurse their young underwater. The offspring are kept very close to the mother and are carefully guarded against lions, leopards, and other predators.

Pigmy hippos are considerably smaller than the *amphibius* species. They inhabit swampy forests in a very small area of western Africa, where they are now considered rare.

Wart Hog

Phacochoerus aethiopicus

Fantastic warts protrude below this wild pig's eyes and on its nose. The protuberances are obvious on the males only, and serve no clearly discernible purpose. The tusks, larger in males, are probably not used in rooting out food, as was once supposed. Rather they protect the wart hog's face from brambles during forays into dense bush and scrub, where the animal kneels and eats the short grasses that grow near the base of taller vegetation. The tusks also serve as weapons during head-to-head battles between rivals. Despite their menacing appearance, however, these mammals are not particularly brave. They prefer simply to trot away from an enemy.

Wart hogs are mostly diurnal. They travel in small parties over the savannahs and light forests of most of Africa. When trotting, they carry the tufted tail straight up.

Young are usually born in the fall, and are not striped like most of the other wild pig newborns. After about a year, they are **154** mature enough to leave their mothers.

▲ Wart hogs, 85 kg
Wild boar, 35–150 kg (females), 75–200 kg (males) ▶

Wild Boar

Sus scrofa

The wild boar is the most widely distributed of all wild pigs, at least five species being found in southern Europe, northern Africa, and southern Asia. It can survive in many habitats, but prefers dense undergrowth. A wild boar rooting for food improves the soil by aerating it, but can also cause severe property damage. Except for yearlings and older males, wild boars are gregarious. Parties of six to ten wander in the evening or by night, searching for food, and may cover great distances.

Prior to the rutting season the adult male develops reinforced areas on his sides, to protect him from rivals' canines. During courtship the boar circles around the sow, massaging her with his snout and making rhythmic noises, which may induce her to remain still. After mating, the boar returns to his solitary life style, and the sow, after about 113 days, bears between three and eleven piglets, which she guards closely. The newborns have longitudinal stripes, a coloration probably inherited from their distant ancestors. The fact that their parents are *not* striped is thought to reflect long-range changes in the habits and habitat of the species—a shift, for example, from a shadowy habitat, where stripes would camouflage, to more open country, where they are no longer necessary.

Bactrian Camel

Camelus bactrianus

The two-humped Bactrian camel and the one-humped drome-
dary are the largest members of the family Camelidae, which
also includes the daintier vicuñas, llamas, guanacos, and al-
pacas. Only the Bactrian camel is still found in the wild—it
inhabits desert and steppe areas of Mongolia and Chinese Tur-
kestan, where it is officially protected.

Camels are a study in adaptation to drought. Their nostrils
close to keep out sand and dust, and the groove that runs
between each nostril and the cleft upper lip channels moisture
from the nasal passages into the mouth. Contrary to popular
notion, camels do not store water in their humps. They need to
drink every four or five days, but can tolerate dehydration of up
to a quarter of their body weight. At such times their humps
shrink and may lean to one side. Reduced perspiration and
concentrated urine also help conserve moisture.

Like dromedaries, Bactrian camels have broad-soled feet that
are ideal for maneuvering in sand, and they move their front and
hind legs on the same side in unison, which accounts for their
156 rolling gait.

Bactrian camel, 450–700 kg

Selected Bibliography

Burt, William Henry, and Grossenheider, Richard P. *A Field Guide to the Mammals*, 2nd ed. The Peterson Field Guide Series. Boston. Houghton Mifflin, 1964.

Burton, Maurice, ed. *The World Encyclopedia of Animals*. New York. T. Y. Crowell, 1972.

Cahalane, Victor H. *Mammals of North America*. New York. Macmillan, 1966.

Carrington, Richard. *The Mammals*. Life Nature Library. New York. Time-Life Publications, 1963.

De Vore, Irven, and Eimerl, Sarel. *The Primates*. Life Nature Library. New York. Time-Life Publications, 1965.

Grzimek, Bernhard, ed. *Grzimek's Animal Life Encyclopedia*, vols. 10–13. New York. Van Nostrand Reinhold, 1972–75.

McIntyre, Joan, ed. *Mind in the Waters: A Book to Celebrate the Consciousness of Whales and Dolphins*. A Sierra Club Book. New York. Scribner's, 1974.

Matthews, L. Harrison. *The Life of Mammals*. 2 vols. New York. Universe Books, 1969.

Murie, Olaus J. *A Field Guide to Animal Tracks*. The Peterson Field Guide Series. Boston. Houghton Mifflin, 1964.

Sanderson, Ivan. *Living Mammals of the World*. New York. Doubleday, 1975.

van den Brink, F. H. *A Field Guide to the Mammals of Britain and Europe*. The Peterson Field Guide Series. Boston. Houghton Mifflin, 1968.

van Gelder, Richard. *Biology of Mammals*. New York. Scribner's, 1969.

Walker, Ernest P., *et al*. *Mammals of the World*, 3rd ed. 2 vols. Baltimore. The John Hopkins Press, 1975.

Williams, John G. *A Field Guide to the National Parks of East Africa*. The Peterson Field Guide Series. Boston. Houghton Mifflin, 1968.

Index

Mary Parker Buckles, former Series Editor of the National Audubon Society's Nature Bulletins, has written and edited numerous educational pamphlets and guidebooks on plant and animal life. A native of Mississippi, Ms. Buckles now resides in Columbia, Missouri, where she pursues a lifelong interest in the flora and fauna of the United States through freelance writing and photography.